TEACHER'S MANUAL AND ANSWER BOOK

HAYES EXERCISES IN READING COMPREHENSION

GRADE 1 (BOOK A)

By Peter J. Ketchum

No. BR921

Teacher's Manual and Answer Book for Exercises in Reading Comprehension, Grade One, Level A.

This teacher's Manual has been prepared for the exclusive use of the teacher and is not supplied to pupils at any time.

Page 1: Hide-and-Seek (Phrase Meaning/Directional)

(1) on the farm; (2) in the hay; (3) behind a tree; (4) in the barn; (5) in the house.

Students are asked to draw a picture of a hiding place.

Page 2: A Birthday (Phrase Meaning/Reading for Detail)

(1) on the steps; (2) with a ball; (3) with a big hat; (4) on his lap; (5) next to Mike.

Mike should be circled. Ask students why.

Page 3: A Lost Boat (Phrase Meaning/Reading for Detail)

(1) in the house; (2) under the bed; (3) over the bed; (4) in the box.

The boat is **in the sink.** The boat should be circled.

Page 4: What Am I? (Phrase Meaning/Drawing Inferences)

(1) I live **in the barn.** I walk **on four feet.** I have a tail **behind me.** I give milk **to you.** I am a **cow.**

(2) I lay eggs **in a nest.** I fly **in the sky.** I eat worms **for lunch.** I walk **on two feet.** I am **a bird.**

(3) I live in a **house.** I sleep **on a bed.** I go **to school.** I am a **boy.**

Page 5: Who Saw It? (Phrase Meaning/Reading for Details)

The words circled are: (1) under the chair; (2) by a dog; (3) for a week.

Dad and Pam (man rebus/girl rebus) saw the cow.

The cow was with the spoon (rebus).

Page 6: Farm and Zoo (Classifying)

Zoo animals: zebra, giraffe, monkey, elephant, lion, camel, tiger. All should have an **X** on them.

A line should be drawn from house to dog.

Page 7: Bees and Peas (Classifying/Initial b and p/Following Directions)

Students write the letter **b** and **p.**

Students circle: ball, bat, boy, bed, bag, bell

Students circle: pan, pin, pot, pig, pad, pen, pie

Page 8: Mud Pies (Sentence Meaning/Context)

(1) Tim plays in the mud. (2) He makes pies. (3) The sun is hot. (4) It makes the pies hard.

Tim will **not** eat the **mud** pies.

Page 9: Mrs. Fixit (Sentence Meaning/Part and Whole Relationships)

(1) Mrs. Fixit fixes things. (2) She fixes a bike. (3) She fixes a bell.

Students make a drawing of a stuffed toy.

Page 10: Pick a Name (Main Idea/Titling)

(1) Huff, Puff, and Pop!; (2) A Trip to the City; (3) A Bad, Bad Cat (**Cat and the Milk** might be chosen.); Justify choice of title. (Determine why **A Bad, Bad Cat** tells more.); (4) Late for School; (5) A Magic Bed.

Page 11: Name a Story (Main Idea/Titling)

(1) Mom's Birthday; (2) A Brave Dog; (3) Dick's Dragon; (4) Jane's Picture of Jane.

Students draw a self-portrait.

ANSWER KEY — PULL TO REMOVE

Page 12: A Mix Up

(1) A night Trip; (2) Mike's Apple Pie; (3) Bill's First Plane Trip; (4) Amy, the Apple.

Page 13: What Is It About? (Inferences/Classifying)

(1) letters, stamps, schoolbus (optional answer), bag; (2) girl, dog, boy; (3) ball, waves, rain, umbrella; (4) store, desk, hat, clown (optional answer)

Answers might vary. Let students defend their choices.

Page 14: What It WILL NOT be about (Inferences/Main idea/Classifying)

(1) worm; (2) boat; (3) chair; (4) dog.

Students will draw a picture of their houses.

Page 15: What Do You Eat? (Main Idea)

(1) Picture c; (2) Picture c; (3) Picture c; (4) Picture c.

Students put an X on what they like to eat.

Page 16: Hot and Cold (Main Idea/Classifying)

(1) B; (2) C; (3) B or C.

Students will put an X on fire and sun.

Page 17: Things That Go (Main Idea/Inferences)

(1) car; (2) plane; (3) sailboat; (4) train; (5) child; (6) Answer will vary.

Page 18: What Comes First? (Sequencing/First Event/Following Directions)

(1) A; (2) C; (3) A; (4) C.

Students will draw two faces. Angry face first.

Page 19: What Happens Next? (Sequencing)

(1) 1, 2; (2) **2, 1**; (3) **2, 1**; (4) **1, 2**; (5) **2, 1**; (6) **2, 1**; (7) **2, 1**; (7) **2, 1**; (8) **2,1.**

Page 20: What Happens Last (Sequencing/Conclusions)

(1)B; (2) A; (3) B; (4) A; (5) B; (6) A.

Page 21: Tell a Story (Sequencing/Drawing Conclusions)

(A) 2/1/3; (B) 2/1/3; (C) 1/3/2; (D) 2/1/3.

Page 22: Guess What They Saw? (Inferences)

(1) elephant; (2) turtle; (3) kitten; (4) apple; (5) fish; (6) Z; (7) Paul saw them in a book.

Page 23: Help Is on the Way (Predicting Outcomes)

(1) doctor; (2) bus driver; (3) policeman; (4) ladder; (5) Most students will answer YES.

Page 24: Bad Bill and the Box (Paragraph Meaning/Ordering)

(A) 2/1/3; (B) 1/3/2; (C) 3/1/2; (D) 2/1/3.

Page 25: Take Tim Home (Sequence/Following Directions)

Students should draw a "road" from 1 to the car, from the car to the barn, from the barn to a horse, from the horse to a train, from the train the students should draw tracks to Tim's house.

Page 26: What Am I? (Inferences/Detail)

(1) faucet; (2) pencil; (3) light bulb; (4) tub; (5) television. Students will write a riddle.

Page 27: Mad, Glad, and Sad (Inferences/Judging Feelings)

(1) sad; (2) glad; (3) mad; (4) glad.

Page 28: Bugs and Dinosaurs (Initial b and d/Classifying)

Students will write the letter **b** and the letter **d.**

Students circle: box, bed, bear, boy, balloon, barn, bud

Students circle: dog, deer, door, dot, duck, doctor, doll

Page 29: What Bob and Sue See (Main Idea)

(1) Bob and Sue see a ring. (2) Sue picks it up. (3) Sue gives it to a policeman. (4) The Lost Ring.

Page 30: Up and Down (Main Idea)

The main idea is: Bill helps Tim fly a kite.

Page 31: Things That Go Fast (Main Idea)

(1)b; (2) b; (3) c; (4) c.

Students will draw a picture of something they ride.

Page 32: No Fish in the Tub, Please (Classifying)

Students put X on: duck, soap, boat, brush, boy, plug, bubbles

Students put a circle on: fish, snail, plant, rock, food

Students put fish in the bowl.

Page 33: Bad, Bad Dogs (Main Idea/Details)

(1) a/c/d; (2) b; (3) a/c; (4) a/c/d/e.

Page 34: Look and See (Noting Details/Classifying)

(1) b/d; (2) a/d; (3) a/b; (4) a/c/d; (5) a/d; (6) a/c/d.

Page 35: Jim and Sue at the Circus (Main Idea/Details)

(1) a/c; (2) a/d; (3) c; (4) b; (5) a.

Page 36: Make It Go (Context/Verb Choice/Sentence Meaning)

(1) walks; (2) swim; (3) fly; (4) jump; (5) jumps; (6) swims; (7) hop.

Page 37: What Goes Here? (Context/Noun Choice)

(1) letter; (2) penny; (3) flag; (4) milk; (5) baby.

Page 38: Hit His Hat (Word Discrimination/Vowels)

(1) hat; (2) hot; (3) hit; (4) hop; (5) hen; (6) hay.

Students should put an X on the pot.

Page 39: A Big Bug in a Bag (Word Discrimination/Vowels)

(1) big; (2) bug; (3) bag; (4) bad; (5) bed; (6) bud.

Students should put an X on the bag.

Page 40: Pat and Her Pet (Word Discrimination/Vowels)

(1) pet; (2) pot; (3) pat; (4) pie; (5) pig; (6) paw.

Students should mark the dog and the paw.

Page 41: A Mouse in the House (Word Discrimination)

(1) moon; (2) spell; (3) house; (4) spill; (5) room; (6) mouse.

Students should write, in this order, **mouse** and **house.**

Page 42: Bags (Main Idea/Inferences)

(1) C; (2) D; (3) B; (4) A.

Students will draw a face on a bag.

Page 43: How Can You Tell? (Main Idea/Details That Support or Illustrate Main Idea)

(1) Circle NO The ball is **d.** (2) Cirlce NO The house is **d.**

Page 44: What Is It About? (Main Idea)

(A) Lee grows many things. (B) Bob likes pets. (C) We get things from the farm.

Page 45: Do You Have A Tail? (Word Relationships/Vocabulary)

(1) a/b/c/d; (2) a/b/c/d/f; (3) a/c/d/e; (4) a/b/d; (5) a/b/c.

Page 46: Then and Now (Time Relationships/Sequencing)

(A) 2/1; (B) 1/2; (C) 1/2; (D) 2/1; (E) 2/1; (F) 1/2.

Page 47: A Happy Ending (Predicting Outcomes)

(1) b; (2) a; (3) b; (4) a; (5) Students draw an ending.

Page 48: Who Did It? (Predicting Outcomes)

Yes should be circled on both. **Tom** should be circled. (Point out muddy feet and relate them to the rain outside.)

ANSWER KEY — PULL TO REMOVE

Hide-and-Seek

Look at each picture. Then read each sentence. Circle the best ending for the sentence.

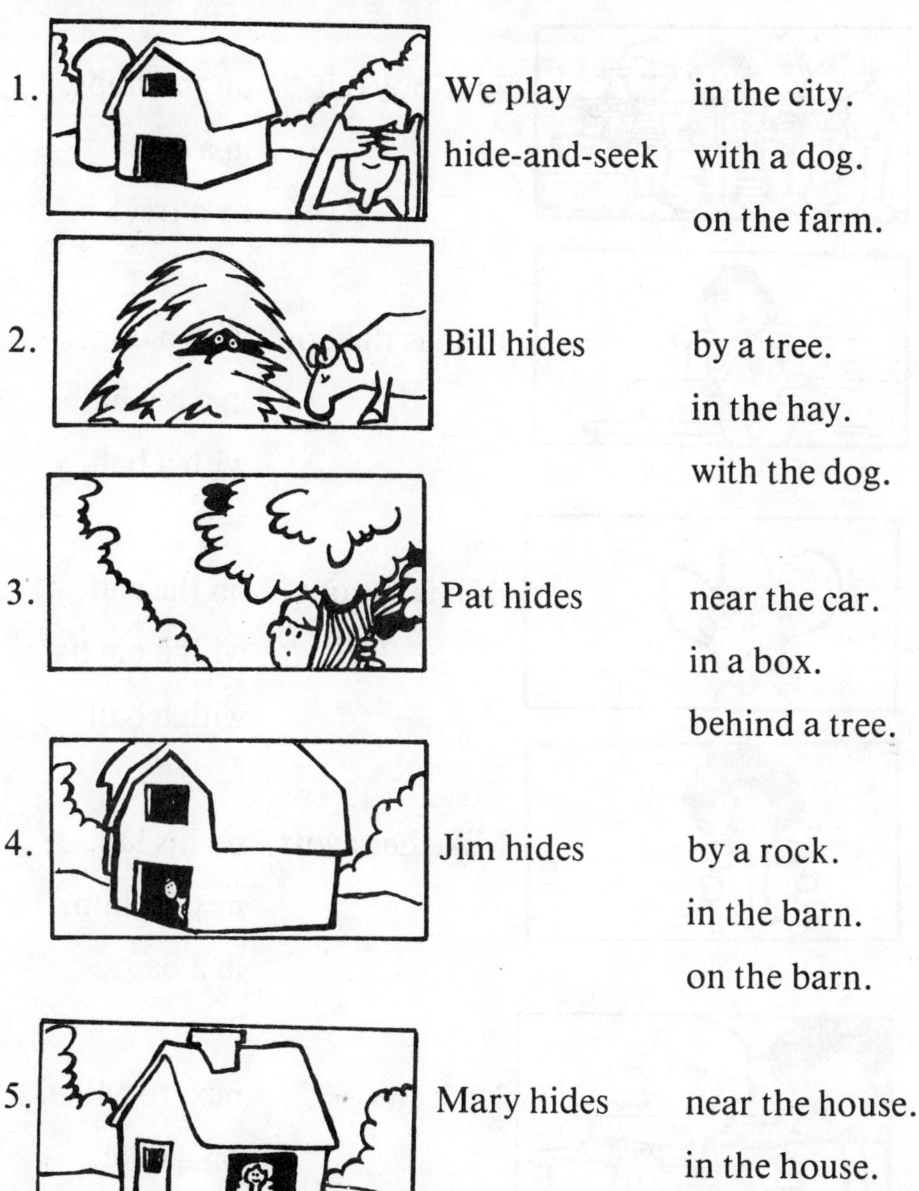

1. We play hide-and-seek
   - in the city.
   - with a dog.
   - on the farm.

2. Bill hides
   - by a tree.
   - in the hay.
   - with the dog.

3. Pat hides
   - near the car.
   - in a box.
   - behind a tree.

4. Jim hides
   - by a rock.
   - in the barn.
   - on the barn.

5. Mary hides
   - near the house.
   - in the house.
   - on the house.

Where would you hide? Draw a picture.

A Birthday

Look at each picture. Then read each sentence. Circle the best ending for each sentence.

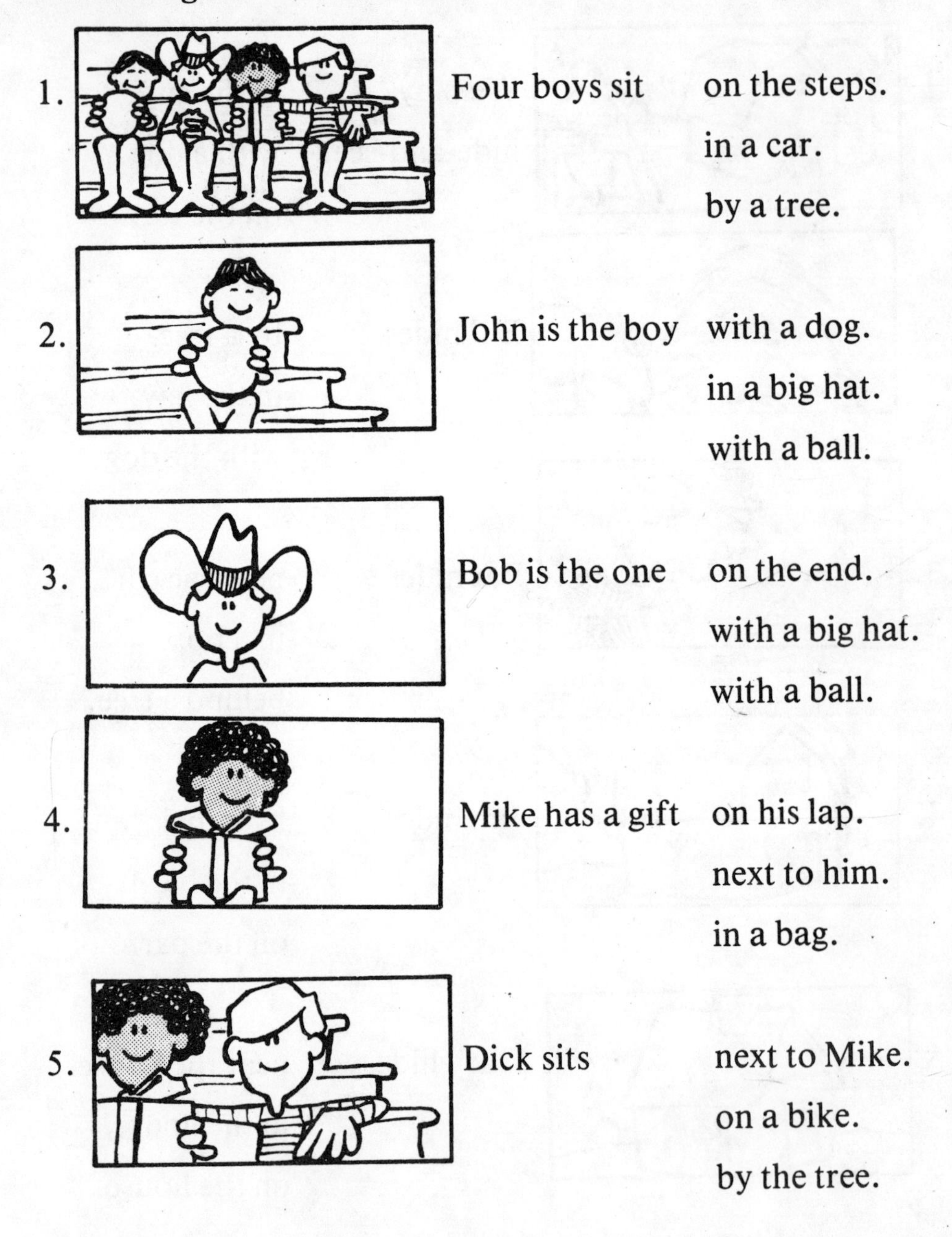

1. Four boys sit — on the steps. / in a car. / by a tree.

2. John is the boy — with a dog. / in a big hat. / with a ball.

3. Bob is the one — on the end. / with a big hat. / with a ball.

4. Mike has a gift — on his lap. / next to him. / in a bag.

5. Dick sits — next to Mike. / on a bike. / by the tree.

Which boy has a birthday today? How can you tell? Circle the boy who has a birthday.

A Lost Boat

Look at each picture. Read what it is about. Draw a line to the best ending for each sentence.

1. 

Bill looks for his boat

in the house.
by a car.
at school.

2. 

He looks

under the bed.
on the chair.
in the box.

3. 

Bill looks

over the bed.
near the bed.
under the bed.

4. 

He looks

on the chair.
in the box.
near a table.

Bill looks and looks. **Help him find the boat. End the sentence.**

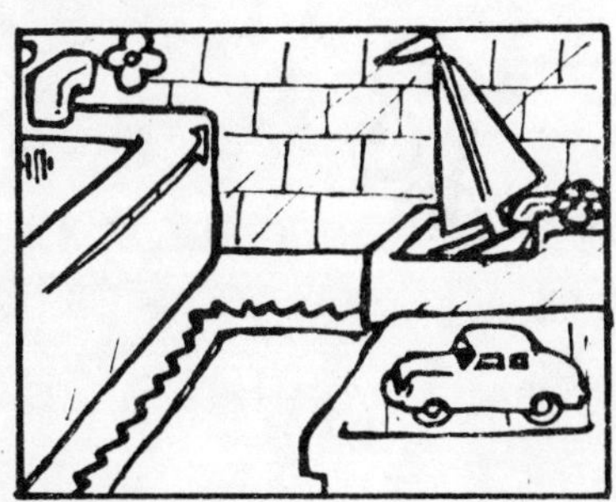

The boat is

in the car.
near the sink.
under the rug.
in the sink.
by the tub.

Draw a circle around the boat.

What Am I?

Draw a line to the best ending.

1. I live
   I walk
   I have a tail
   I give milk

   on four feet.
   to you.
   in the barn.
   behind me.

I am a   

2. I lay eggs
   I fly
   I eat worms
   I walk

   for lunch.
   on two feet.
   in a nest.
   in the sky.

I am a   

3. I live
   I sleep
   I go

   on a bed.
   to school.
   in a house.

I am a   

Who Saw It?

Circle the words that do not tell about the story.

1\.

under the chair

with a cow

at night

2\.

with Dad

by a dog

in a car

3\.

into the car

by my nose

for a week

Who saw the cow?

Who was with the cow?

Farm and Zoo

Some animals live on a farm. Some live in a zoo. **Put an X on the zoo animals.**

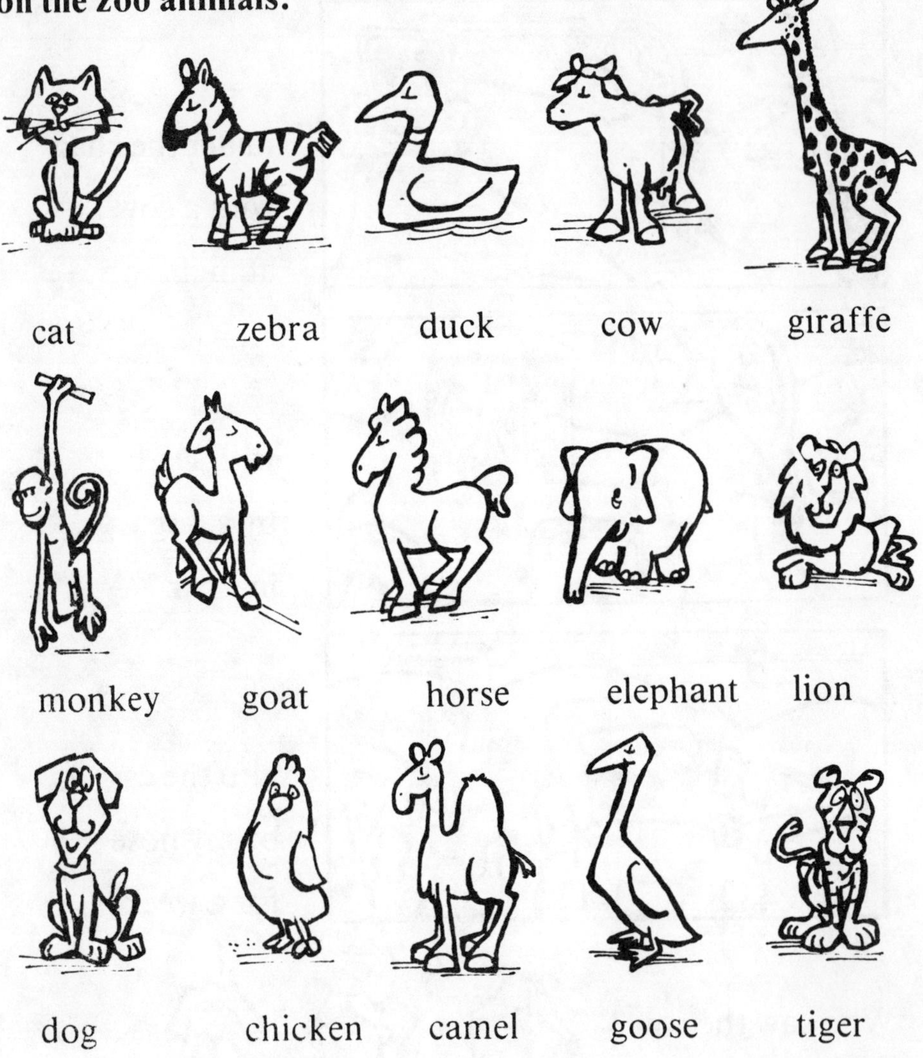

Draw a line to the animal who lives here.

Bees And Peas

Write the letter b.

Write the letter p.

Circle the words that begin with the same sound as bee.

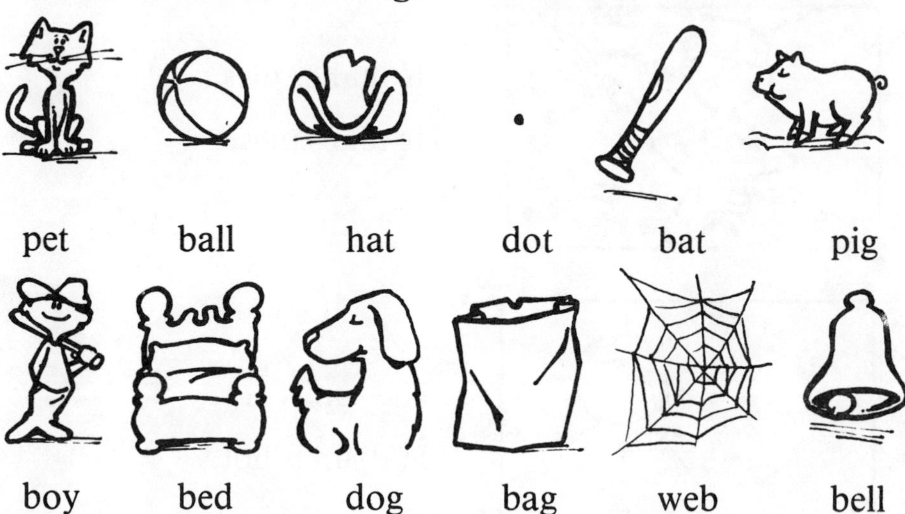

Circle the words that begin with the same sound as pea.

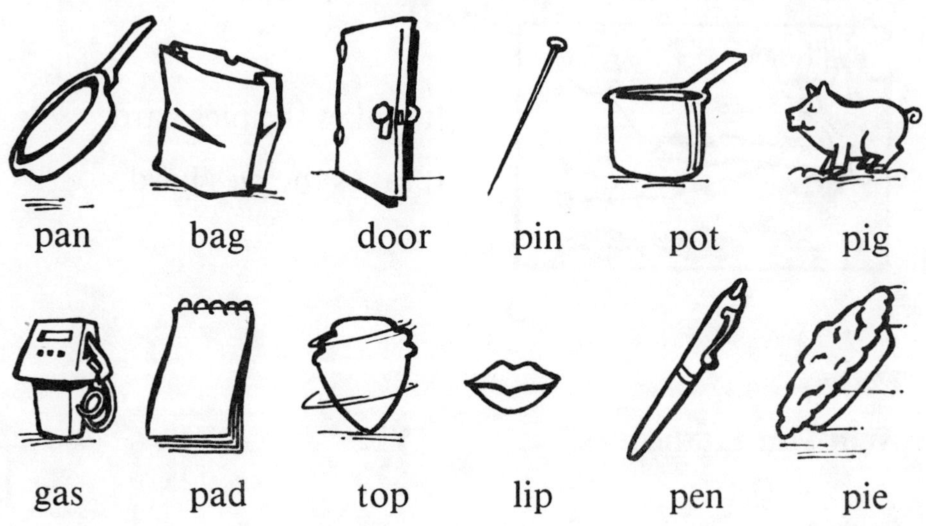

Mud Pies

Circle the words that tell about each picture.

1. 

Tim stays in the mud.

Tim plays in the mud.

2. 

He makes pies.

He takes pies.

3. 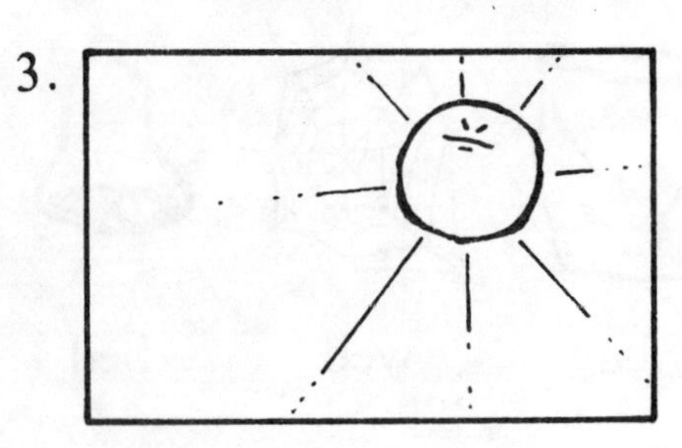

The sun is not.

The sun is hot.

4. 

It makes the pies hard.

It takes the pies hard.

Will Tim eat the pies? **YES** **NO**

Mrs. Fixit

Draw a line to the words that tell about the picture.

1.

Mrs. Fixit hits things.

Mrs. Fixit fixes things.

2.

She fixes a bike.

She fixes a kite.

She fixes a door.

3.

She fixes a toy.

She fixes a bell.

She fixes a ball.

Mrs. Fixit wants to fix this. **Can you help? Show her how**

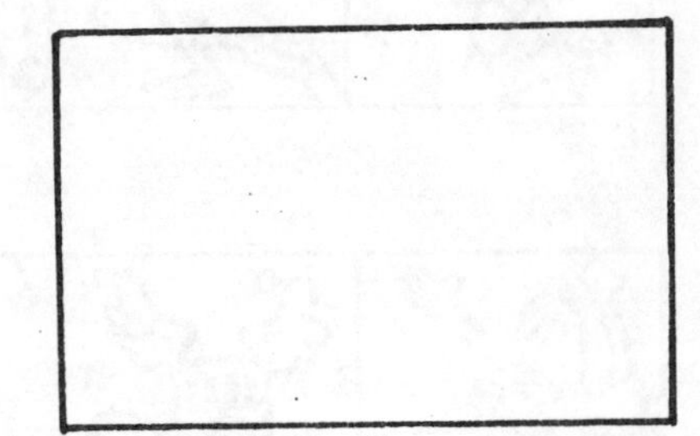

Pick a Name

Look at each story. Circle the best name for the story.

1.

Huff, Puff!

Huff, Puff, and Pop!

Pop, Huff, Puff

2.

Mom and I Go Away

A Trip to the City

About the Trip

3.

A Cat and the Milk

A Bad, Bad Cat

A Bad, Bad Dog

4.

Late for Lunch

Early for School

Late for School

5.

Time for Bed

A Magic Bed

Jill Goes to Bed

Name a Story

Look at each story. Draw a line to the best name for each one.

1.

2.

Jane's Picture of Jane

3.

A Brave Dog

Mom's Birthday

4.

Dick's Dragon

Draw a picture of you.

A Mix Up

Ooops! The name of each story is wrong. **Draw a line to the right story.**

Bill's First Plane Trip

1.

Amy, the Apple

2.

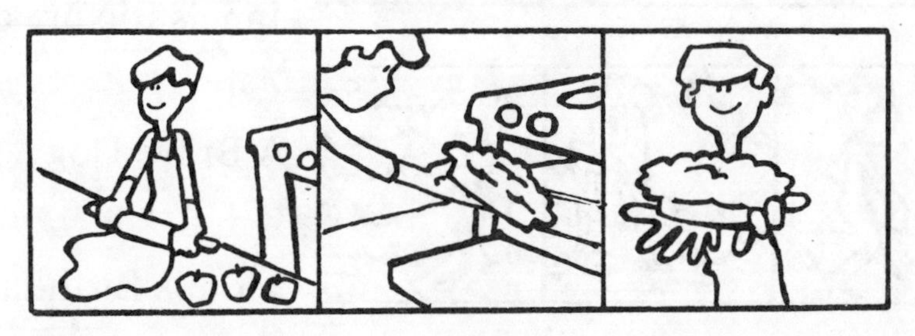

A Night Trip

3.

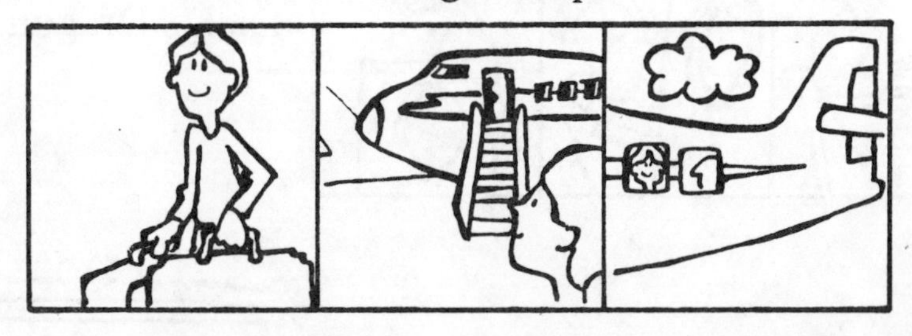

Mike's Apple Pie

4.

What Is It About?

Read the name of the story. Put an X on the things the story probably will tell about.

What It Will Not Be About

Read the name of the story. Put an X on the things the story will not tell about.

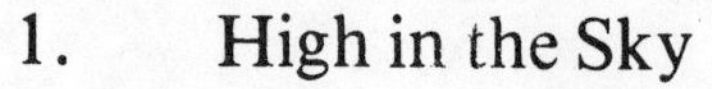

1. High in the Sky

worm balloon plane bird rocket

2. Under the Sea

fish boat diver clam octopus

3. In the Ground

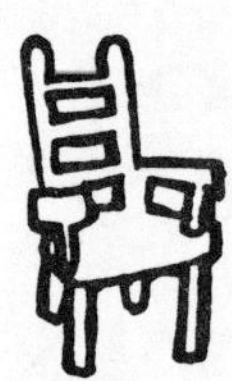  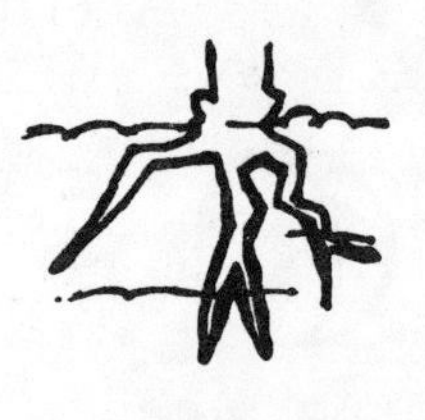

carrot worm chair ant root

4. Things That Live in Dark Places

bat ant dog bear snake

Draw a picture of where you live.

What Do You Eat?

Read the story. Circle the picture that tells the most about the story.

1. A frog sits. It sees a bug. It eats the bug.

A.  B.  C. 

2. A bird sits. It sees a worm. It eats the worm.

A.  B. 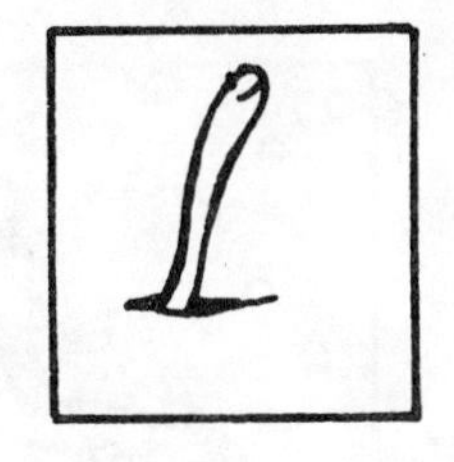 C. 

3. A dog sits. It sees a cake. It eats the cake.

A.  B.  C. 

4. Lee sits. He sees an apple. He eats the apple.

A.   B.  C. 

What do you like to eat?

Hot and Cold

Read the story. Put an X on the picture that tells the most about the story.

1. Mary runs. The sun is hot. Mary is hot. Mary stops.

A. 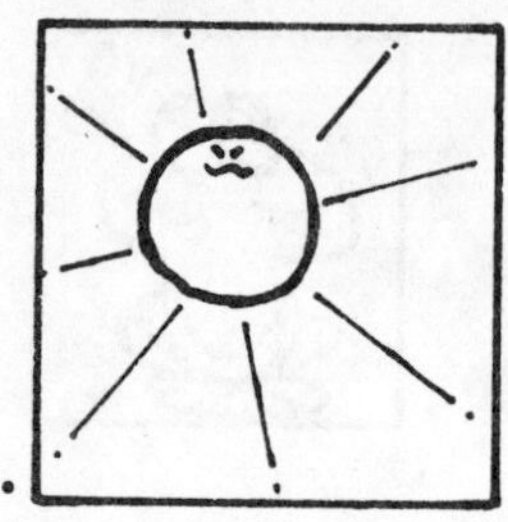
B. 
C. 

2. It snows. Jim makes a ball. He makes two balls. He makes a snowman.

A. 
B. 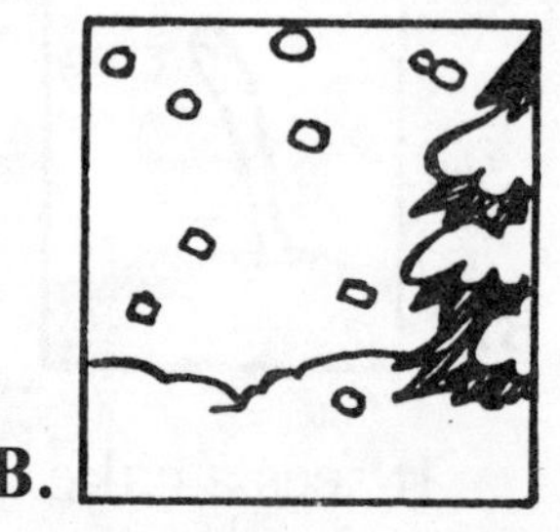
C. 

3. There is a fire. The firemen come. They put it out.

A. 
B. 
C. 

Put an X on the things that are hot.

Things That Go

Read the story. Circle the answer.

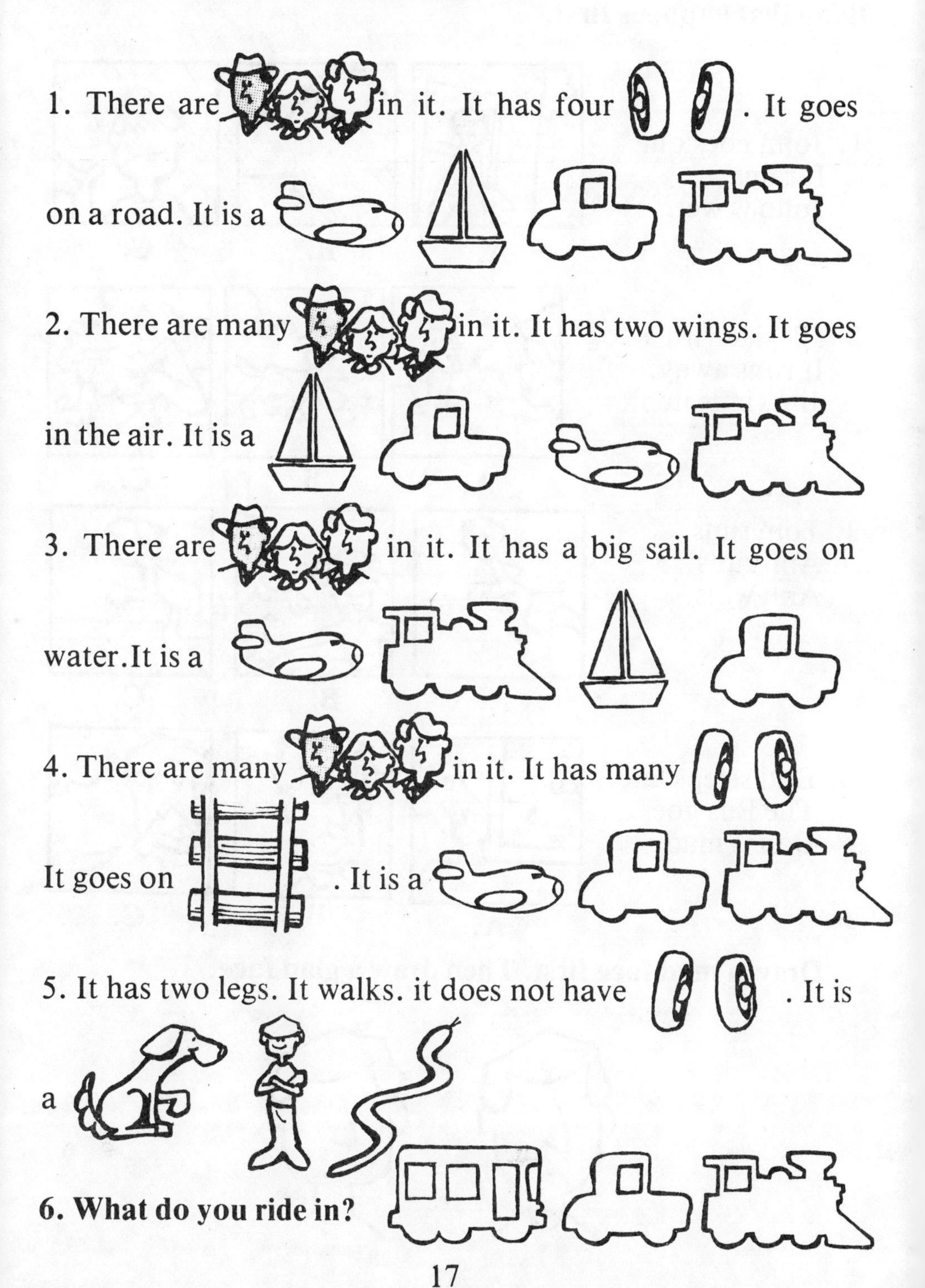

1. There are [picture] in it. It has four [picture]. It goes on a road. It is a

2. There are many [picture] in it. It has two wings. It goes in the air. It is a

3. There are [picture] in it. It has a big sail. It goes on water. It is a

4. There are many [picture] in it. It has many [picture] It goes on [picture]. It is a

5. It has two legs. It walks. it does not have [picture]. It is a

6. What do you ride in?

What Comes First?

Read the story. Look at the pictures. Put an X on the thing that happens first.

1. John goes out.
   It rains.
   John is wet.

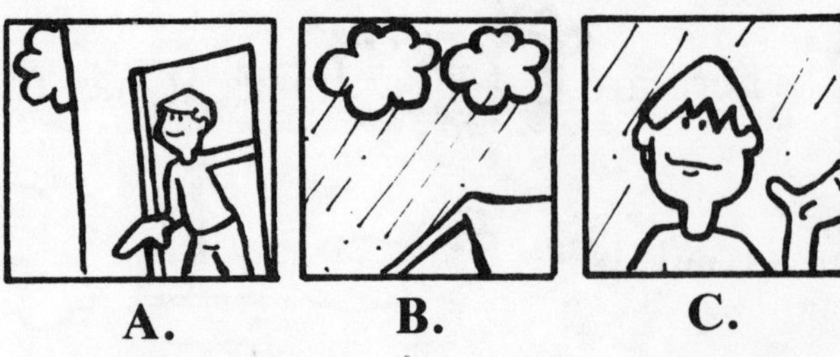

A. B. C.

2. Jill sits with a dog.
   It runs away.
   Jim finds it.

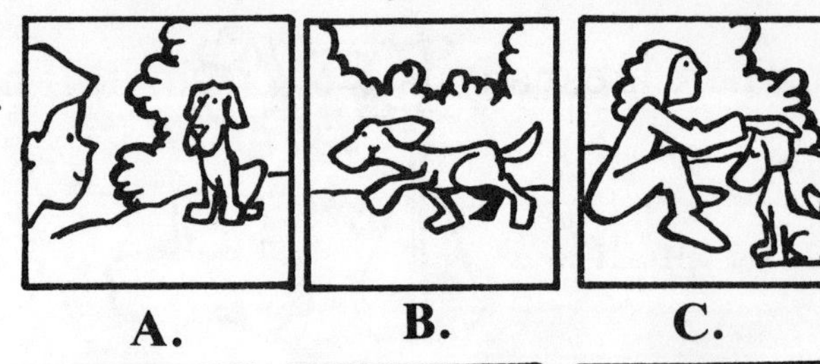

A. B. C.

3. Tom runs.
   Ann runs.
   Ann wins.

A. B. C.

4. Dad sleeps late.
   The Bus goes.
   Dad is mad.

A. B. C.

Draw a mad face first. Then draw a glad face.

What Happens Next?

Write 1 if it happens first. Put 2 if it happens next.

(1) ______ Joe has a cup. ______ Joe fills it.

(2) ______ Sam has a cut. ______ Sam fell down.

(3) ______ Sue sees a bird. ______ Sue looks up.

(4) ______ The cat goes away. ______ The mouse is glad.

(5) ______ Paul hears Ben. ______ Ben calls Paul.

(6) ______ Tim gets up. ______ Tim sleeps.

(7) ______ Lee eats. ______ Mom makes lunch.

(8) ______ It is dark. ______ The sun sets.

What Happens Last?

Put an X on the part that happens last.

Tell A Story

Put 1, 2, or 3 on the pictures to tell a story.

Guess What They Saw?

What did they see? Put a circle around it.

1. Pam saw it. It was very big. It was an

2. Tom saw it. It was slow. It was a

3. Lee saw it. It was soft. It was a

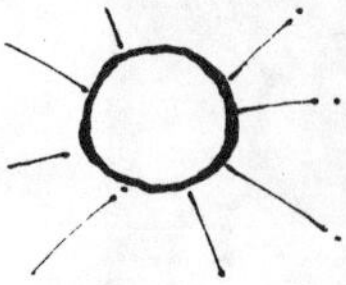

4. Jill saw it. It was red. It was an

5. Bob saw it. It was wet. It was a

6. Sam saw it. It was last. It was a

7. Paul saw all of these things. He saw them in a

Help Is on the Way

Put an X on the best ending for the story.

1. Bill is hot. Bill is sick. He will go to a

2. The bus comes. Jane gets on it. She sees the

3. Tom is lost. He is sad. He will go to a

4. A cat is in a tree. It is sad. Dick sees it. He gets a

5. Will Dick get the cat down? YES NO

Circle the answer.

Bad Bill and the Box

Make a story. Write 1 on the words that start the story. Write 2 on the words that come next. Write 3 on the words that come last.

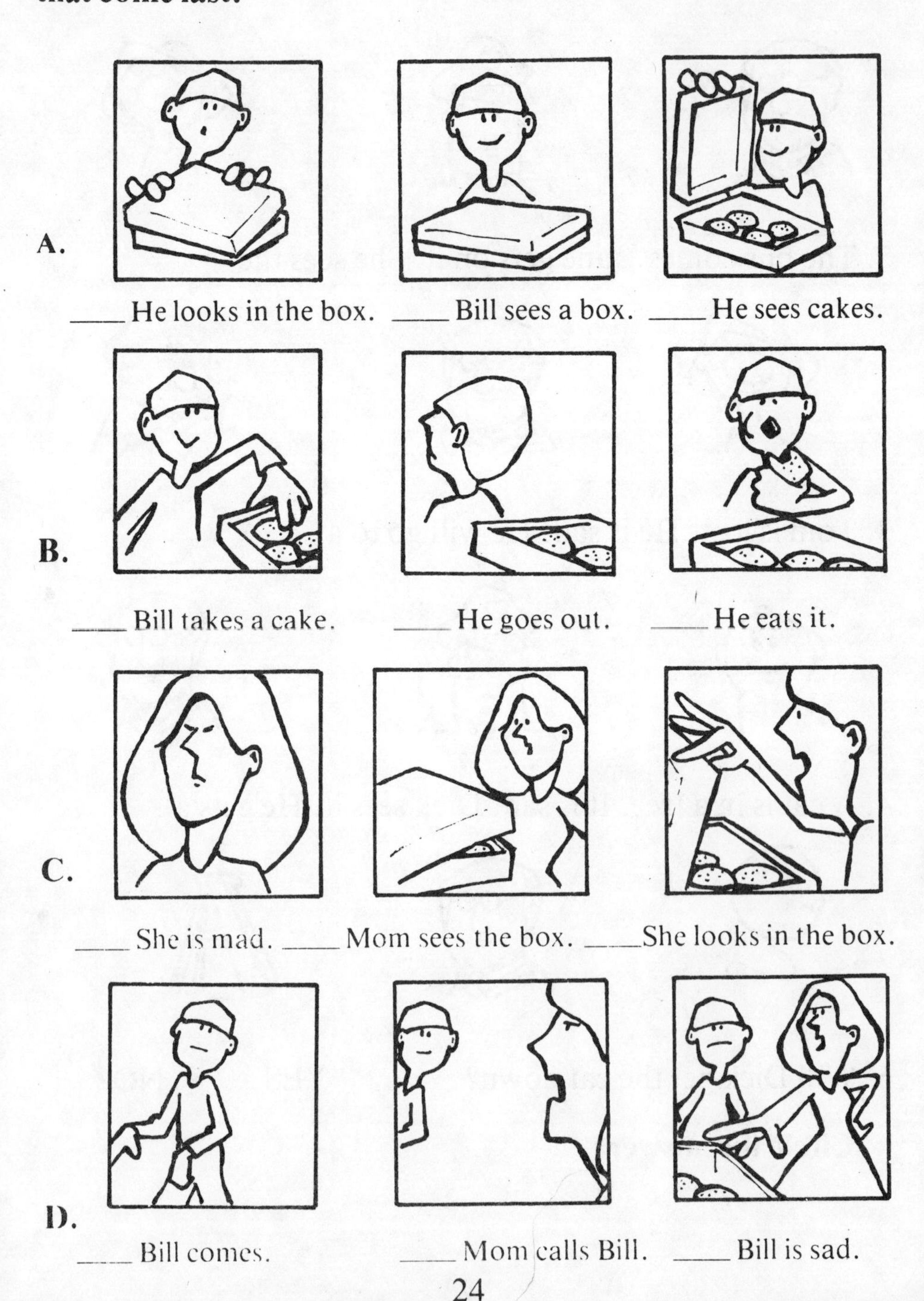

A.

____ He looks in the box. ____ Bill sees a box. ____ He sees cakes.

B.

____ Bill takes a cake. ____ He goes out. ____ He eats it.

C.

____ She is mad. ____ Mom sees the box. ____ She looks in the box.

D.

____ Bill comes. ____ Mom calls Bill. ____ Bill is sad.

Take Tim Home

Help Tim. He is lost. Start at 1. Make a  to the  . Drive the 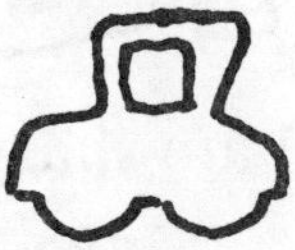 .

Make a  to the  .

Get a  . Draw a  to it. Ride the  to a  . Draw a  to the  . Take the  to Tim's  .

Draw a  to it.

What Am I?

Put a circle around the best answer.

1. I am hot. I am cold. I am wet. I am dry.

I am a

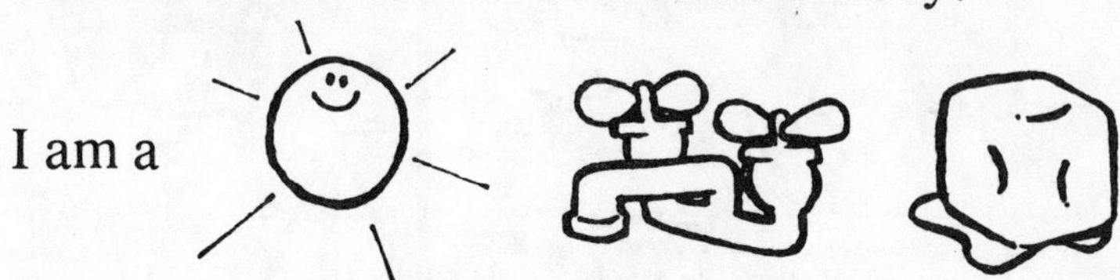

2. I am long. I get short. I am sharp. I can write.

I am a

3. I am light. I am dark. I am on. I am off.

I am a

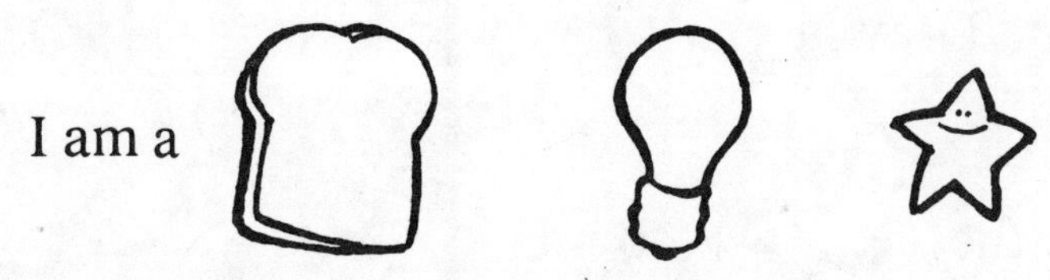

4. I am full. I am empty. I am wet. I am dry.

I am a

5. I am on. I am off. You see me. I do not see you.

Tell a riddle about a

I am ______________________________

I am ______________________________

Mad, Glad, and Sad

Look at the pictures. Draw a face about the story. Make the face mad  **, glad**  **or sad.** 

1.

2.

3.

4.

Bugs and Dinosaurs

Write the letter b. **Write the letter d.**

Circle the words that begin with the same sound as bug .

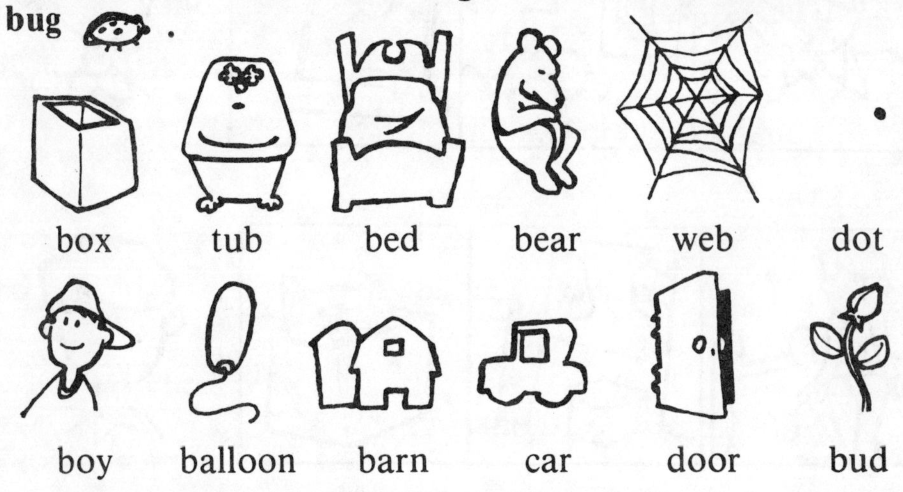

Circle the words that begin with the same sound as dinosaur .

What Bob and Sue See

Put X on the words that tell about the picture.

1. ____ Sue sees a ring.

   ____ Bob sees a ring.

   ____ Bob and Sue see a ring.

2. ____ Sue and Bob pick it up.

   ____ Sue picks it up.

   ____ It is still there.

3. ____ Bob gives it to a policeman.

   ____ Bob gives it to a mailman.

   ____ Sue gives it to a policeman.

Put X on a good name for this story.

4. ____ Let's Go on a Walk

   ____ A Good Luck Ring

   ____ The Lost Ring

   ____ The Last Ring

Up and Down

Read the story. Put an X on the words that tell the most about the story.

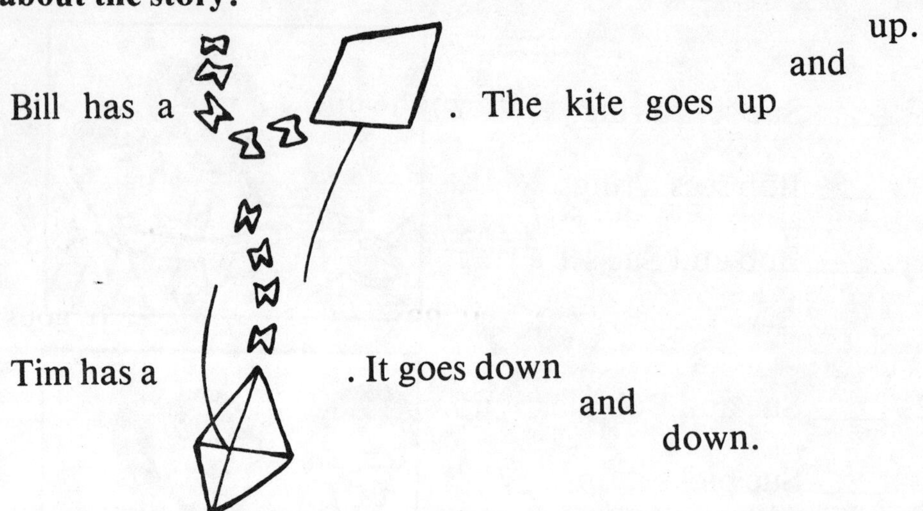

Bill has a [kite]. The kite goes up and up.

Tim has a [kite]. It goes down and down.

Tim is [sad]. Bill goes to Tim. Bill helps Tim.

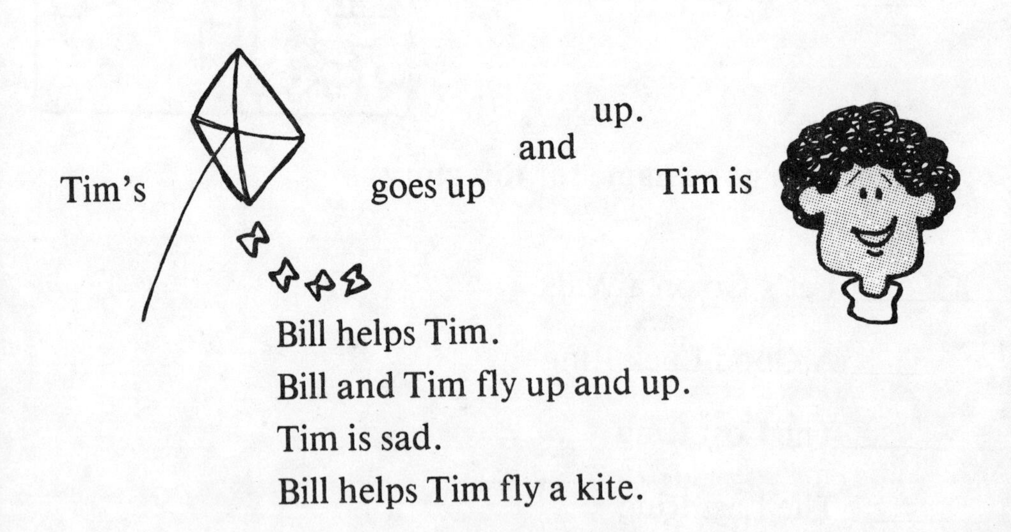

Tim's [kite] goes up and up. Tim is [happy].

Bill helps Tim.

Bill and Tim fly up and up.

Tim is sad.

Bill helps Tim fly a kite.

Things That Go Fast

Read the story. Put an X on the best answer.

1. Pam has a [sled]. It goes fast. It goes in [snow]. It goes down the hill.

   This story is about **a.** **b.** **c.**

2. Jim has a [bike]. It has two [wheels]. It goes fast.

   This story is about **a.** **b.** **c.**

3. Sue has [skates]. They are like [shoes]. They have wheels. They go fast.

   This story is about **a.** **b.** **c.**

4. Mom and Dad have a [bike]. It has two [seats]. It goes fast.

   This story is about **a.** **b.**

   c.

What do you ride that goes fast?
Draw a picture of it.

No Fish in the Tub, Please

Put an X on the things you find here.

Circle the things you find here.

duck (toy) fish snail soap

boat plant brush rock

boy food plug bubbles

Put the  **where it goes. Draw a picture there.**

Bad, Bad Dogs

Jill goes on a . Lee goes on a .

Bow and Wow go on a .

Here is what happens.

Put X on the answers.

1. Who went on the ?

   a. b. c. d.

2. What did and play?

   a. b. c.

3. What did and eat?

   a. b. c.

4. What was left?

   a. b. c. d. e.

Look and See

Circle the answers.

1. What is big here ?

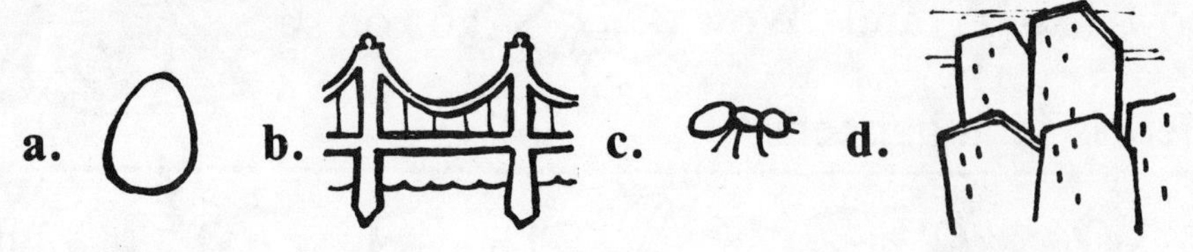

2. What is small here ?

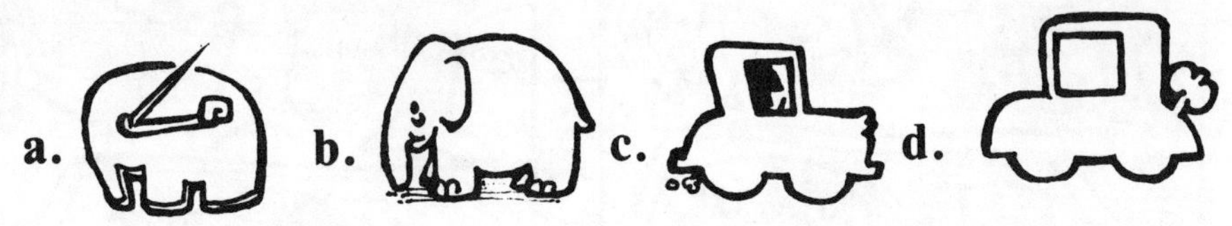

3. What is loud here ?

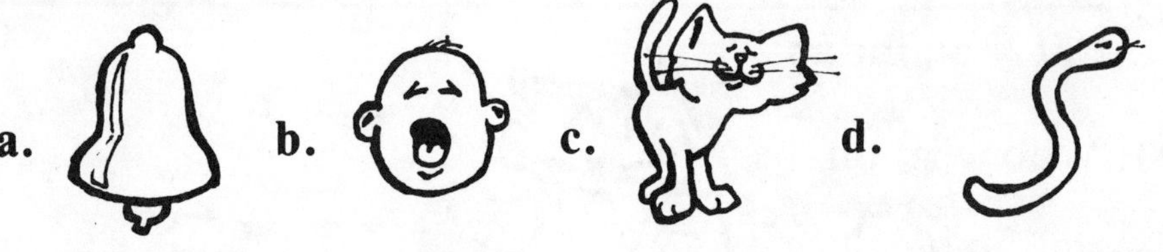

4. What has a ◇ on it ?

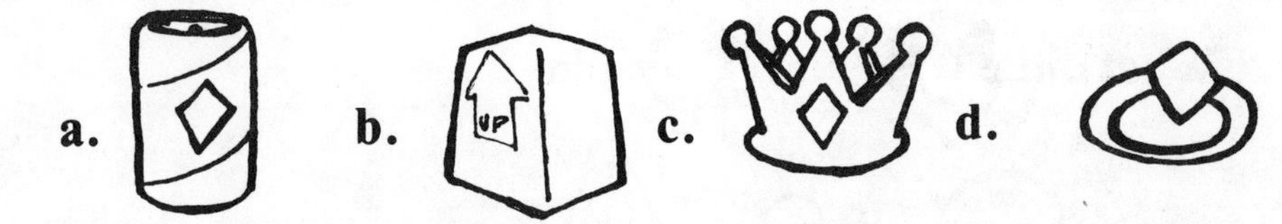

5. What is good to eat ?

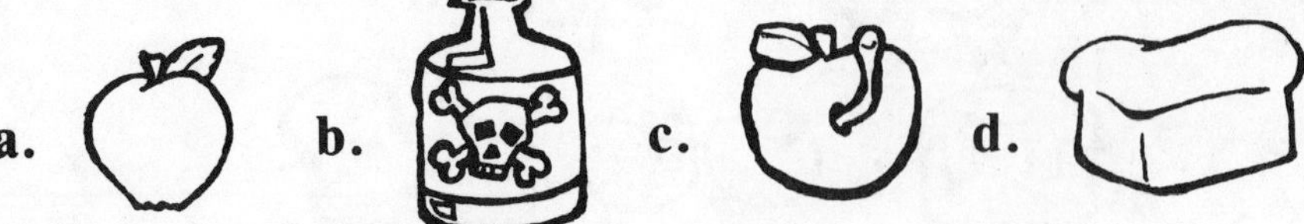

6. What is wet here ?

Jim and Sue at the Circus

Circle the answers.

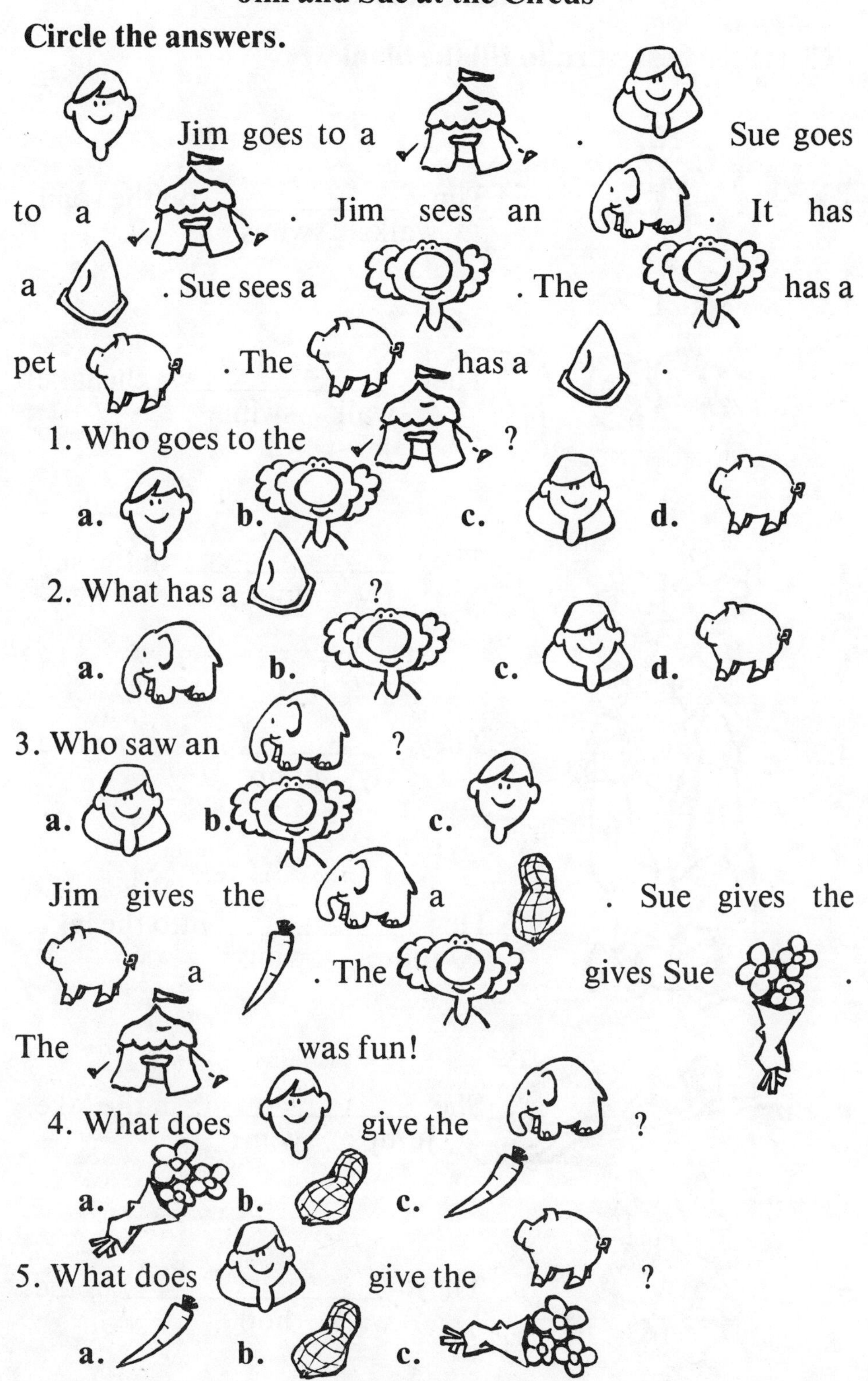

Jim goes to a . Sue goes to a . Jim sees an . It has a . Sue sees a . The has a pet . The has a .

1. Who goes to the ?

a. **b.** **c.** **d.**

2. What has a ?

a. **b.** **c.** **d.**

3. Who saw an ?

a. **b.** **c.**

Jim gives the a . Sue gives the a . The gives Sue . The was fun!

4. What does give the ?

a. **b.** **c.**

5. What does give the ?

a. **b.** **c.**

Make It Go

Circle the best word to fill the blank.

1. Tim ____________ on the road.
   walks swims

2. They ____________ in the lake.
   walk swim

3. They ______________ in the sky.
   fly jump

4. They ____________ on the bed.
   fly jump

5. He ____________ into the lake.
   jumps swims

6. She ______________ in the lake.
   jumps swims

7. They ________________ home.
   walk hop

What Goes Here?

Circle the best word to fill the blank.

1.  A ____________ goes here.

ball    letter    flag

2.  A ____________ goes here.

penny    letter    ball

3.  A ____________ goes here.

letter    flag    penny

4. 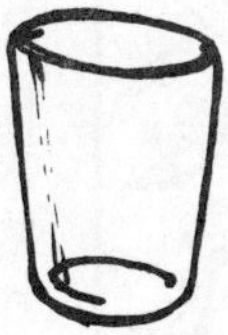 A ____________ goes here.

duck 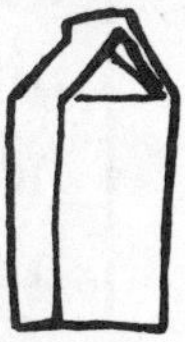   milk    flag

5. 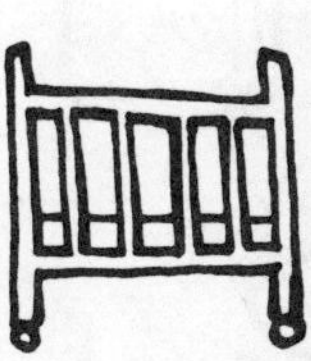 A ____________ goes here.

ball    baby    duck

Hit His Hat

Draw a line to the right word.

1.

pot
hot
hop
hat

2.

hit
hat
hot
has

3.

hat
hop
hit
hip

4.

hot
hop
hit
hat

5.

hem
hip
hen
his

6.

hat
hem
hen
hay

What is his hat?

Put an X on it.

A Big Bug in a Bag

Draw a line to the right word.

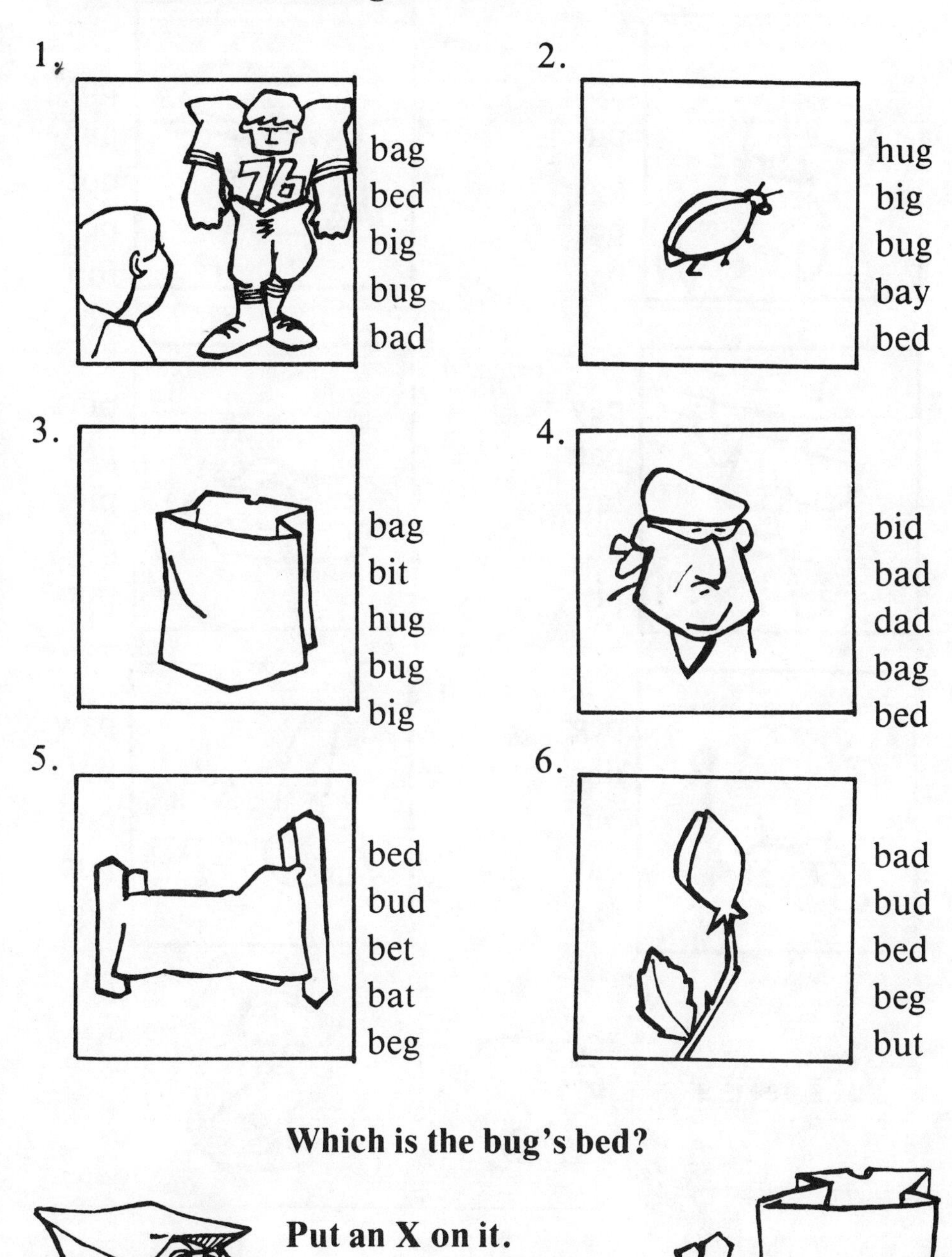

Pat and Her Pet

Draw a line to the right word.

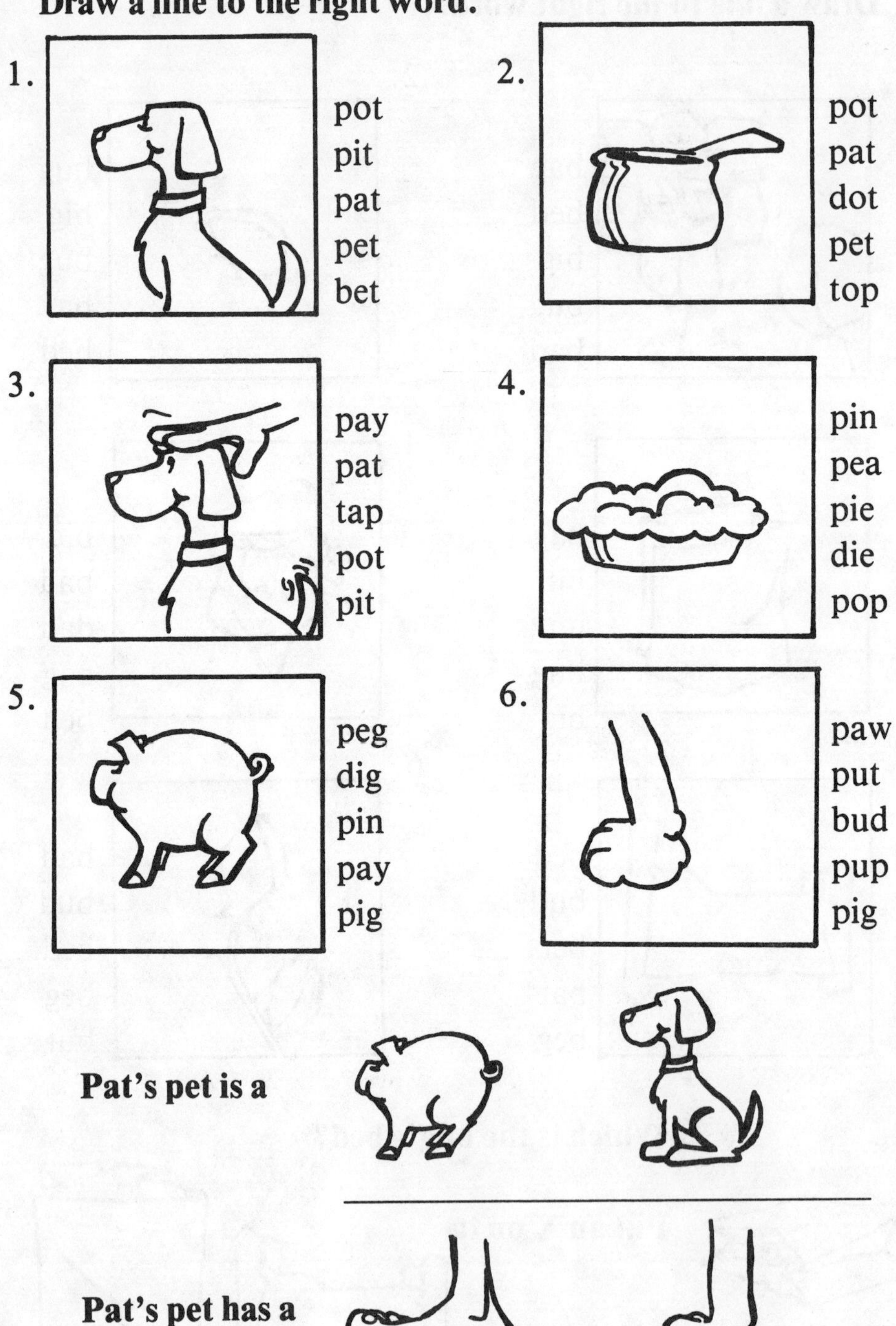

1. pot pit pat pet bet

2. pot pat dot pet top

3. pay pat tap pot pit

4. pin pea pie die pop

5. peg dig pin pay pig

6. paw put bud pup pig

Pat's pet is a ______________________

Pat's pet has a

A Mouse in the House

Draw a line to the word that tells about the picture.

1. 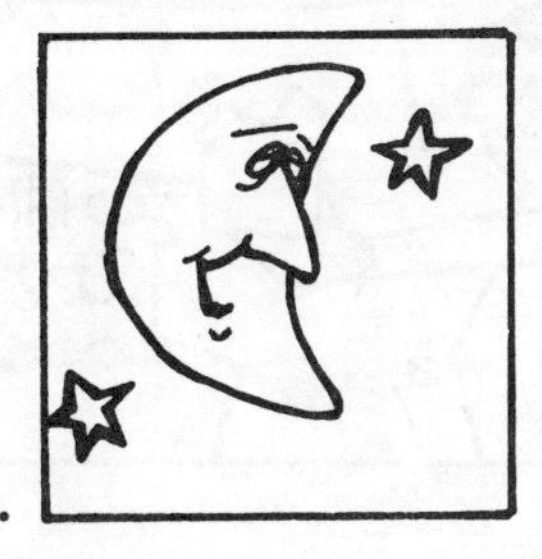

2. 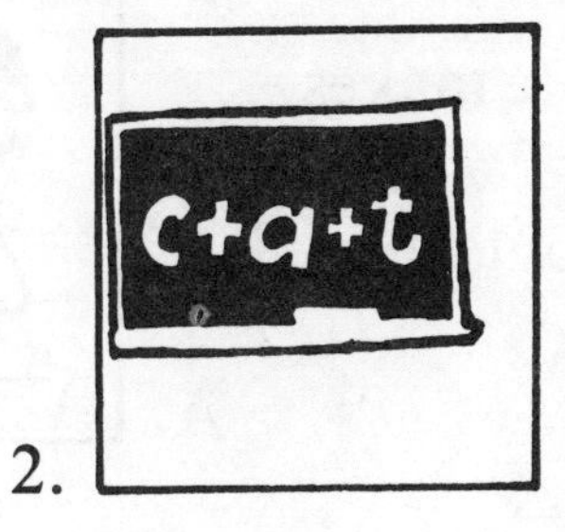

3. 

mouse spell moon

room house spill

4. 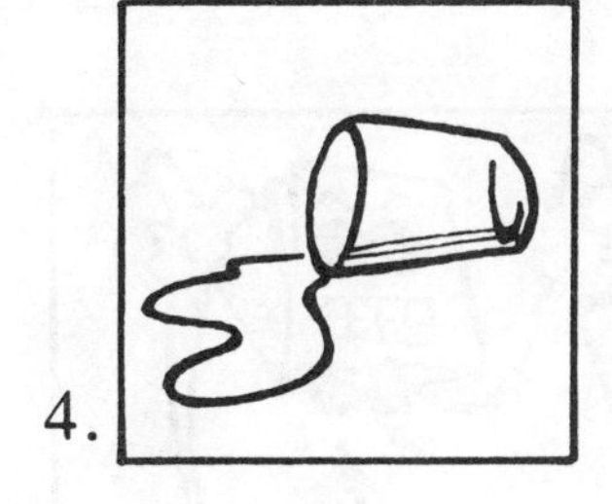

5. 

6. 

Write mouse or house.

There is a ________________

in the ________________.

Bags

Read the story. Draw a line to the  **that tells about the story.**

1. Lee has a bag. He makes a  on it. He puts it on. He will go to a

A.

2. Jill has a bag. She puts a  in it. She puts an in it. She will go to a

B.

3. Bob has a bag. He puts 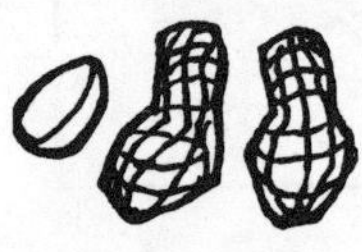 in it. He will go to the

C.

4. Mike has a bag. He puts a  in it. He goes to a

D.

Put a face on this bag. 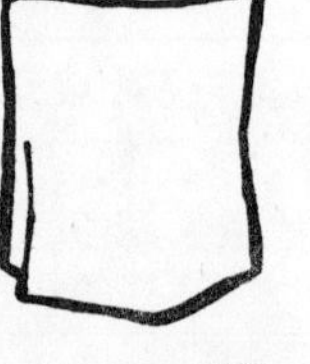

How Can You Tell?

Read the story. Answer the questions.

1. Ben has a ball. Ben lost his ball. It has a on it. It has a on the top. It has a on the bottom.

Jill finds a ball. It looks like this. 

Is it Ben's ball. **Circle the answer.** **YES** **NO**

Can you find Ben's ball? **Put an X on it.**

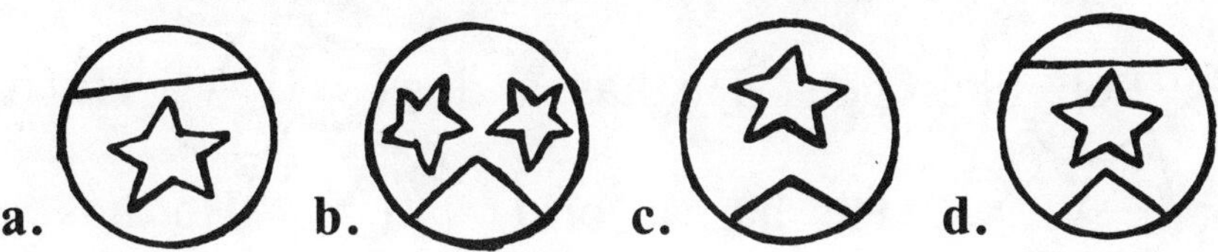

a. **b.** **c.** **d.**

2. Jim looks for Tom's house. It is small. It has two . It has a . There is a

next to it.

Is this the house? 

YES **NO**

Can you help Jim find it? **Put an X on it.**

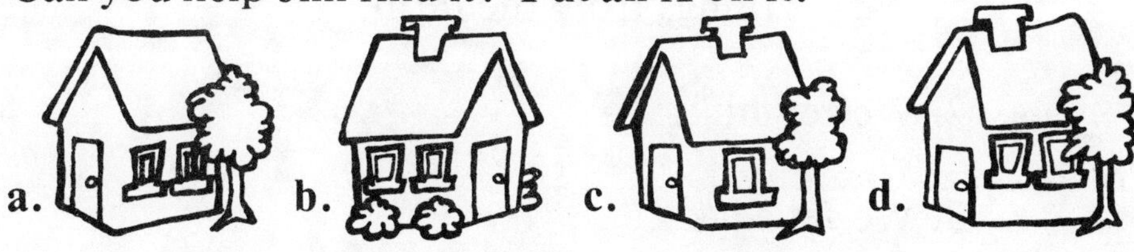

a. **b.** **c.** **d.**

What Is it About?

Read the story. Put X by the words that tell the most about the story.

A. Lee grows many things. She grows peas. She grows. She grows. She even grows a big.

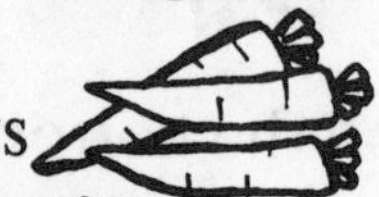

1. Lee grows peas.

2. Lee grows many things.

3. She even grows a big.

B. Bob likes pets. He has a dog. He has a cat. He has a bird. He has some fish.

1. He has a dog.

2. He has some fish.

3. Bob likes pets.

C. We get things from the farm. We get milk.

We get eggs. We get.

1. We get things from the farm.

2. We get milk.

3. We get eggs.

Do You Have A Tail?

1. Circle the things that have a nose.

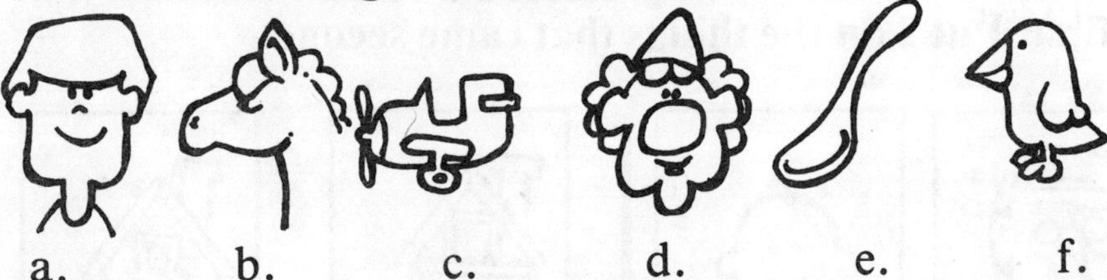

a. b. c. d. e. f.

2. Circle the things that have a tail.

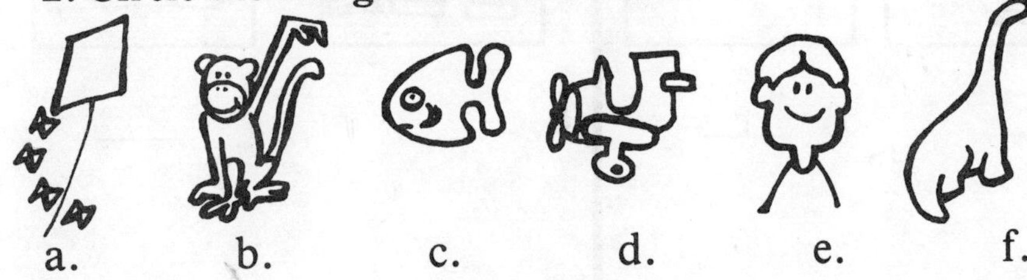

a. b. c. d. e. f.

3. Circle the things that have an eye.

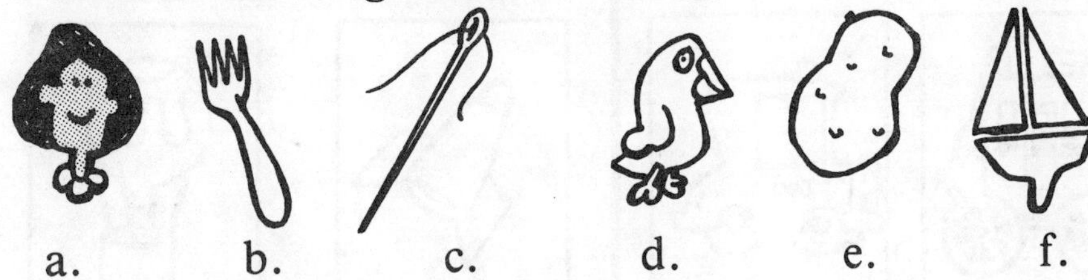

a. b. c. d. e. f.

4. Circle the things that have a leg.

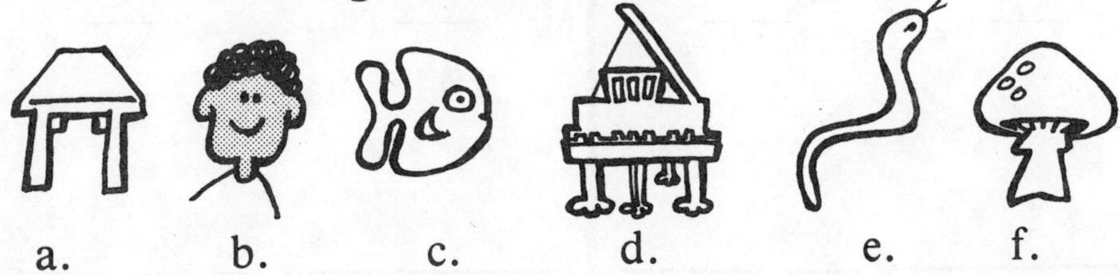

a. b. c. d. e. f.

5. Put an X on the things that you have.

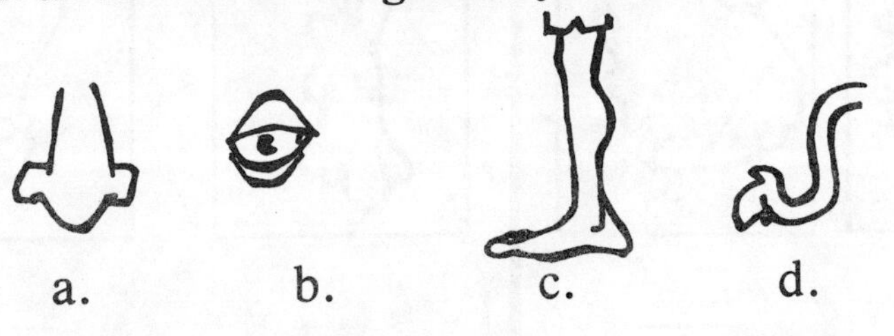

a. b. c. d.

Then and Now

Put a 1 or a 2 under each picture. Put 1 on the things that came first. Put 2 on the things that came second.

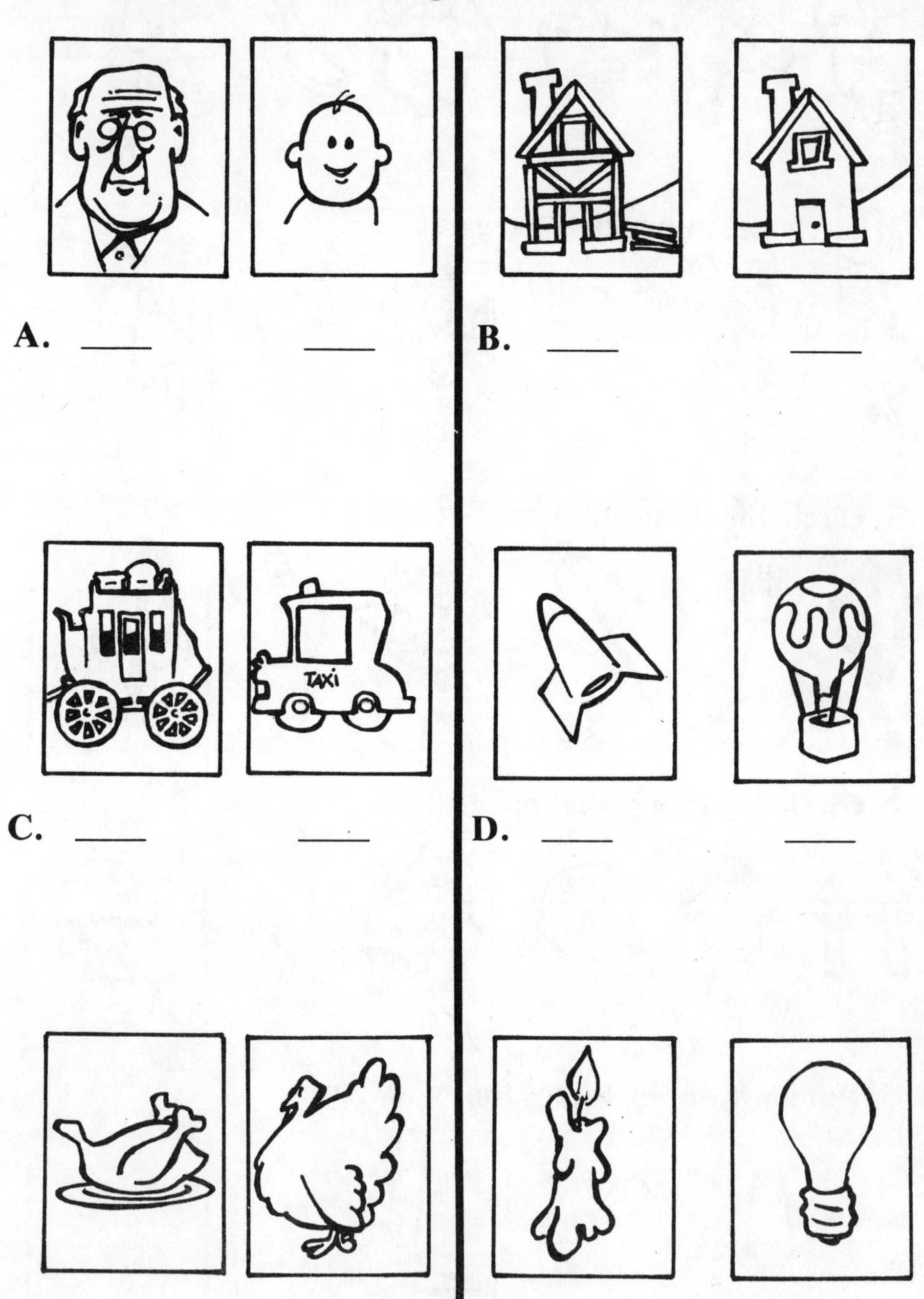

A. ____ ____

B. ____ ____

C. ____ ____

D. ____ ____

E. ____ ____

F. ____ ____

A Happy Ending

Put an X on a happy end for each story.

1. The egg falls.

a. 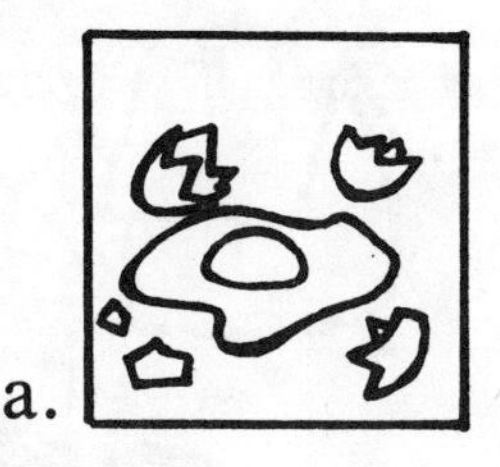 b. 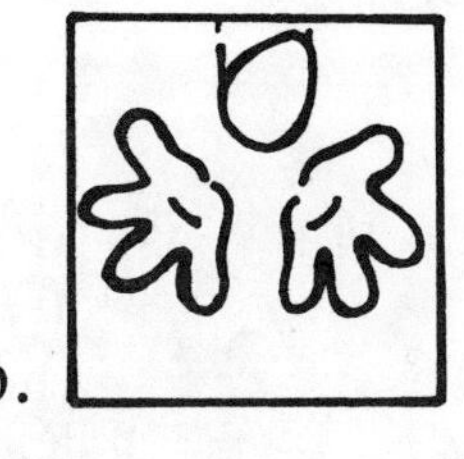

2. A tree is cut.

a.  b. 

3. I bake a cake.

a.  b. 

4. I fish.

a.  b. 

5. **Draw a happy end.**

a. 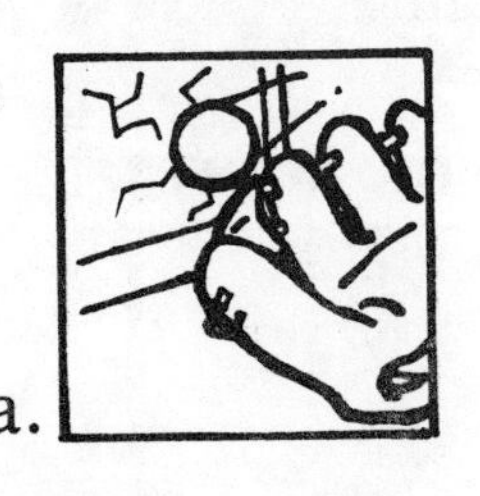 b. 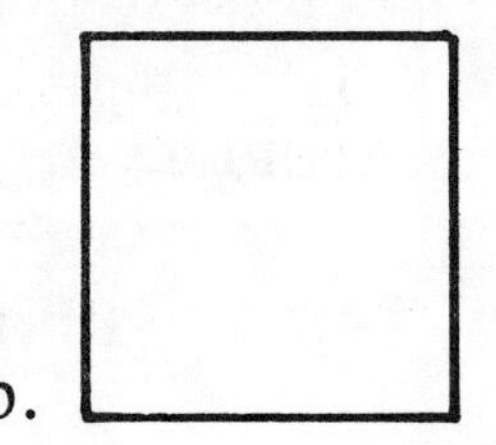

Who Did It ?

This is about Mary, Tom, and Purr  . **Read the story.**

Mary is in the  . It is  . Mary makes a  out of  . It is very tall.

Tom is out. He is wet. He runs to the  .

The sees a  . He runs after the .

What might happen? **Circle Yes or No.**

YES NO

YES NO

Here is what happened.

Who did it? **Circle the answer.**

Tom Purr Mary

Fill the Box

Put an X on the best word for the ☐ .

1. Grandpa is an ☐ man. old tall bad dry

2. Meg got a ☐ dress. old big new sad

3. Bob finds an ☐ hat. new red old tall

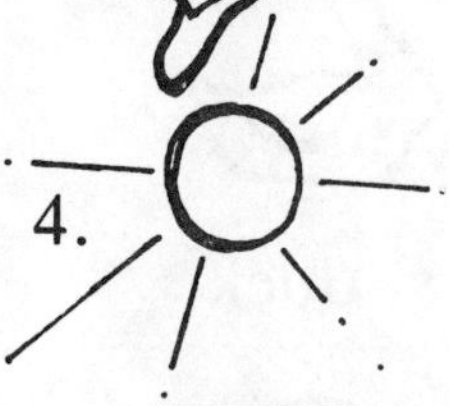

4. We sit in the ☐ sun. cold new hot big

5. Mike is a ☐ boy. good old dry one

6. There is a ☐ apple on the table. red old one dry

Sue has ☐ dogs. one tall two wet

8. Jim has a ☐ ball. red tall bad two

People and Things

Put a box on the people. Put an X on the things.

Are you a ☐ or a X ? **Circle one.**

A Cat, a Ball, and a King

Draw a line under the answer.

The  has a  . The ball had two  on it. A cat sees the  . The cat plays with it. It rolls down the hill. It goes by four  . It stops.

1. **What does the have?** a.  b.  c.

2. **What is on it?** a.  b.  c.  d.

3. **What does it roll by?** a.  b.  c.

Lee sees the  by a  . He takes the ball. He gives it to the  . The  gives Lee a  .

4. **Where does Lee see the ball?** a.  b.  c.

5. **Who does Lee give it to?** a  b.  c.

6. **What does Lee get?** a.  b.  c. d.

Who is Jill? Who is Tom?

I am Jill. I am six. I live in a . I have a dog. I have two . My Dad is a . My Mom is a . I want to be a .

Put a circle on the answer.

1. **How old is Jill?** a. 9 b. 5 c. 6
2. **What are her pets?** a. b. c.
3. **What is her Mom?** a. b. c.
4. **Where do they live?** a. b. c.

I am Tom. I am nine. I live on a . I work on the . I feed the . I feed the .

I want to be an .

5. **Where does Tom live?** a. b. c.
6. **What does he do?** a. b. c.
7. **What does he want to be?** a. b. c.

No School Today

Circle the words that tell the most about each story.

Sue plays all day. She plays 

. She plays with  . She plays with the cat. It is fun.

1. She plays 

.
2. Sue plays all day.
3. It is fun.

Tom works all day. he fixes his  . He makes a . He feeds the . He cuts the .

1. He cuts the .
2. He feeds the dog.
3. Tom works all day.

Draw a picture. Show what you do on a day off.

Who and When?

Put an X on the answer.

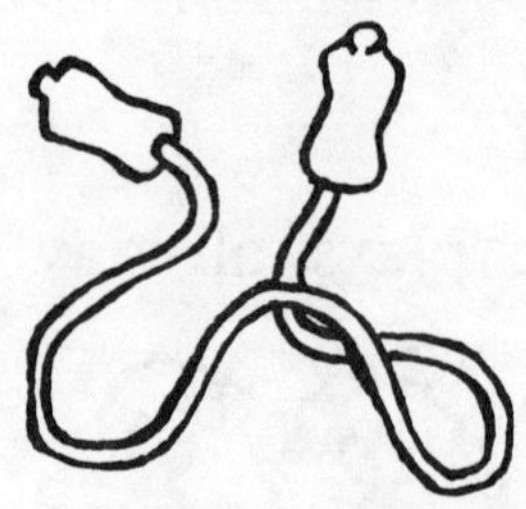

1. We jump rope. Ed jumps . Then Jill jumps. Bill jumps last.

A. **Who goes first?**	Jill	Bill	Ed
B. **Who goes next?**	Bill	Jill	Ed
C. **Who goes last?**	Bill	Ed	Jill

2. We bake cakes. Bob eats one. Then Tom eats one. Pam eats the last one.

A. **Who eats one after Bob?** Pam Bob Tom

B. **Who eats the last one?** Bob Pam Tom

3. Lee comes. He has a cat. Tim comes. He has a dog. The dog barks. The cat runs out. Lee runs out. Tim runs out. The cat is up a tree.

A. **Who comes first?**
Tim cat Lee

B. **Who goes out first?**
cat Tim Lee

C. **Who goes out last?**
Tim Lee cat

How You Grow

Put an X on the words that tell the most about the story.

You need many things to grow. You need food.

You need sleep.

You need exercise. You need water. You need air.

Food works hard for you. It makes strong 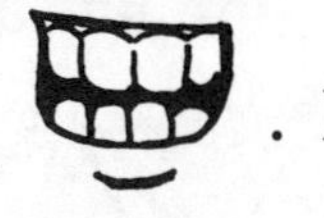. It makes strong . It makes strong .

This story is mostly about:

1. ____ The sun
2. ____ Food
3. ____ What you need to grow
4. ____ How food works

Draw a picture. Show what you had to eat in the morning.

Three Boxes

This story is about:

1. ____ Jim, Bob and a box
2. ____ Things to do with a box.
3. ____ Things to put in a box.

Tell what you can make from a box.

In Tom's Head?

Tom walks on the farm. He sees a  . He sees  . He sees a  .

Jill sees Tom. "Hi, Tom. See the  ? See the  ? See the  ?"

" Tom says, "No. I see a  . I see  . I see a  . Now I see a  .

"Oh, Tom," says Jill. "It is in your head. I see a cat. I do not see a  ."

1. Tom walks on the ____ ____

2. He sees a ____ ____

3. Jill sees a ____ ____

4. Jill does not see a ____ ____

5. **Does Tom really see a  ?** **YES** **NO**

6. **What do you see in your head?**

Where Is It?

1. Tim is on a bus. **Put an X on the things near Tim.**

2. Lee is in a boat. **Put an X on the things far from Lee.**

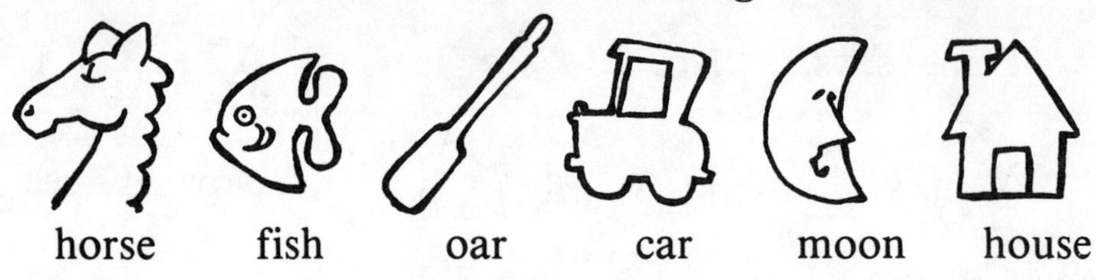

3. Sue is on a plane. **Put an X on the things under her.**

4. Dan is on a train. **Put an X on the things over him.**

What is near you?

What is far from you?

Add a Word

Add a word. Circle it.

1. Bob hits the b____________. 
2. Pam pulls the w____________. 
3. Mary puts on a new d____________. 
4. Jill opens the d____________. 
5. Bill cuts the p____________. 
6. Dad goes on a t____________. 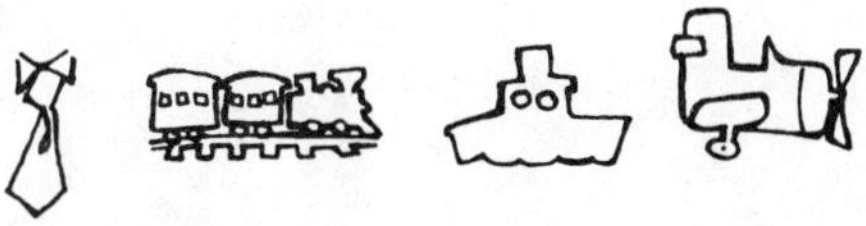
7. Lee makes his b____________. 
8. Tom puts on his b____________.

Pick a Word

Pick a word to fill the □. Put an X on the word.

1. Tim fills his □ with milk. bag glass grass 
2. I □ a fire. spill spell smell 
3. Sue sees a tiny □ in the grass. hog bug bag 
4. Tom puts a □ on the pot. lid lip pot 
5. The □ works in the kitchen. book cook hook 
6. Mary rides a □. house mouse horse 
7. Mom gives me a big □. bug hug hut
8. Would you like a  or a  ?

A Small, Small Town

Dot is a small, small town. It is only a tiny dot on the map. Only two men live in Dot. Mr. Pin is in the big house. Mr. Pip is in the small house. Mr. Pin has a dog. Mr. Pip has a cat.

There are no boys in Dot. There are no girls. There are no cars. There are no trucks. There is only Mr. Pin, Mr. Pip, a dog, and a cat. That is all there is in Dot.

Put a line under the answer.

1. What is the name of the small, small town?

   Dot   Dog   Pin   Pip   Map

2. Who lives in a big house?

   Mr. Pip   Mr. Pin   a boy   a cat

3. Are there cars and trucks?   YES   NO

4. What word tells about Mr. Pin's house?

   big   red   small   tiny   fat

Would you like to live in Dot? Tell why.

Things to Save

Dick saves pins. He has many, many pins. One pin says "I am Dick."  One pin says, "Hi!"

Dick's best pin says, "I love my Mother."

Pam saves stamps.  She has a stamp with a king on it.  She has a stamp with a  on it. She even has a stamp with a  on it.

Put a line under the answer.

1. Dick saves    
2. His best pin says    
3. Pam saves    
4. Pam does not have one with a

Make a stamp.

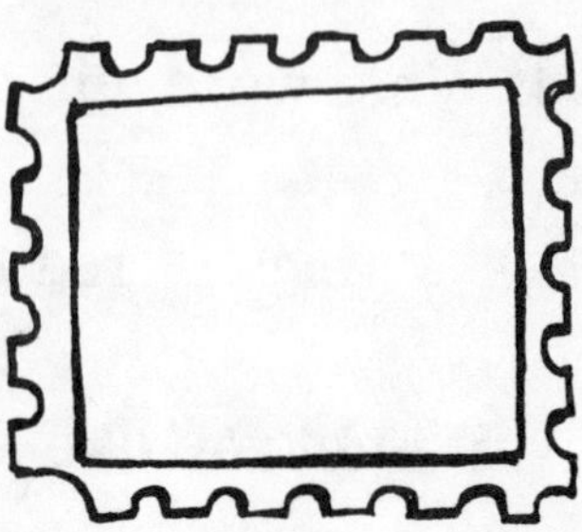

Make a pin.

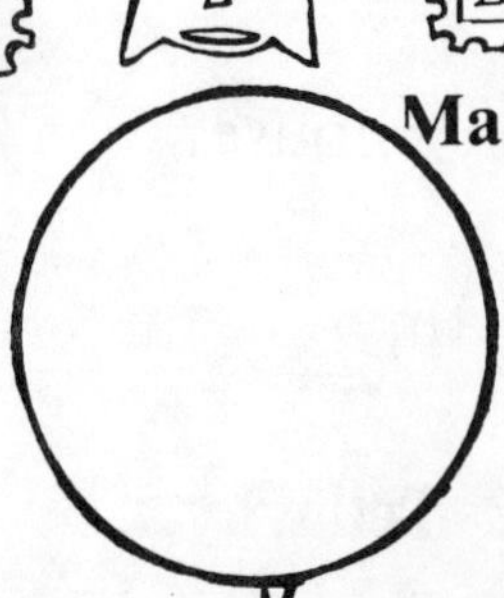

Do Dogs Sing?

Here are the names of books. **Put an X if it might tell a real story. Put an O if it might tell a made-up story.**

1.____ Read about the Moon

2.____ The Very Magic Bike

3.____ Tim Goes to the City

4.____ A Boy on the Moon

5.____ Dan, a Dog Who Sings

6.____ Egbert the Bug King

7.____ The Story of Apples

8.____ Mrs. Big's Little Frog

9.____ What to Do in the Rain

10.____ Bats and Bugs and Things

11.____ How to Feed a Cat

12.____ Make It with Wood

13.____ Hoof, the Sad Horse

14.____ Jill Moves Away

15.____ How to Bake a Cake

16.____ Pam and the Giant

17.____ A Joke on Jim

18.____ Hiss, the Magic Snake

19.____ How Do They Make Bats?

20.____ Who Took a Star?

What is the name of a book you like?

More about Boxes

Tim makes a star. He makes a moon. He makes a . He cuts them out. He puts them in a box.

Jill makes a dog. Jill makes a tree. She makes grass. She makes a moon. She cuts them out. She puts them in a box.

Bob makes a dog. He makes a car and a tree. He makes a moon and some grass . He cuts them out. he puts them in a box.

A. __ B. __ C. __

Put a 1 on Jill’a box. Put a 2 on Bob’s box.

D. **Who did not make a dog?** Jill Tim Bob

Here is a box. Put these in the box.

Page 49: Fill the Box (Word Choice/Context/Adjectives)
(1) old; (2) new; (3) old; (4) hot; (5) good; (6) red; (7) two; (8) red.
Page 50: People and Things (Classifying/Vocabulary/Nouns)
Box = Tom, Meg, Bob, doctor, fireman, cowboy, nurse, girl, Dad ; X = apple, car, milk, Lad, bill, hat, duck, Purr, pail, house, sun. Students = box and should circle it.
Page 51: A Cat, a ball, and a King (Reading to Find Specific Information)
(1) b; (2) c; (3) b; (4) a; (5) b; (6) b.
Page 52: Who Is Jill? Who Is Tom? (Reading for Specific Information)
(1) c; (2) c; (3) b; (4) b; (5) c; (6) b; (7) a.
Page 53: No School Today (Main Idea/Topic Sentence)
(2) Sue plays all day. (3) Tom works all day.
Students draw a picture showing what they do on a holiday.
Page 54: Who and When? (Details about Sequence)
(1) A. Ed; B. Jill; C. Bill; (2) A. Tom; B. Pam; (3) A. Lee; B. cat; C. Tim.
Page 55: How You Grow (Main Idea)
What you need to grow. (3)
Students will draw a picture showing their breakfasts.
Page 56: Three Boxes (Main Idea/Following Directions)
This story is about things to do with a box (2) Students should give ideas for projects with a box.
Page 57: In Tom's Head (Details/Imagination)
(1) farm; (2) dragon; (3) horse, (4) lion; (5) NO; (6) Students will tell what they "see" in their heads.
Page 58: Where Is It? (Inferences/Antonyms)
(1) road/tree/wheel; (2) horse/car/moon/house; (3) house/tree/boat/car; (4) plane/cloud/sun.
Answers will vary for last part of exercise.
Page 59: Add a Word (Initial Consonant Clue/Context)
(1) bat; (2) wagon; (3) dress; (4) door; (5) pie; (6) train; (7) bed; (8) boot; (9) horse; (10) game.
Page 60: Pick a Word (Context)
(1) glass; (2) smell; (3) bug; (4) lid; (5) cook; (6) horse; (7) hug; (8) Students should write **h** for **hug.**
Page 61: A Small, Small Town (Main Idea/Details)
(1) Dot; (2) Mr. Pin; (3) No; (4) big.
Students are asked to discuss story.
Page 62: Things to Save (Details/Main Idea)
(1) pins; (2) I love my Mother; (3) stamps; (4) kangaroo.
Students are asked to draw a pin and a stamp.
Page 63: Do Dogs Sing? (Distinguishing between Fact and Fiction)
(1) X; (2) O; (3) X; (4) O; (5) O; (6) O; (7) X; (8) O (X possible); (9) X; (10) X; (11) X; (12) X; (13) O (X possible); (14) X; (15) X; (16) O; (17) X; (18) O; (19) X; (20) O.
Allow room for debate on each of the titles. Some can only be fact, others fiction. Some might be both. Let students justify their answers.
Page 64: More about Boxes (Main Idea/Predicting Outcome/Reading for Details)
(A) 1; (B) -; (C) 2; (D) Tim.
Students are asked to draw in details in a box. (You might wish to introduce the word diorama).